THE TEACH YOURSELF BOOKS
EDITED BY LEONARD CUTTS

FORESTRY

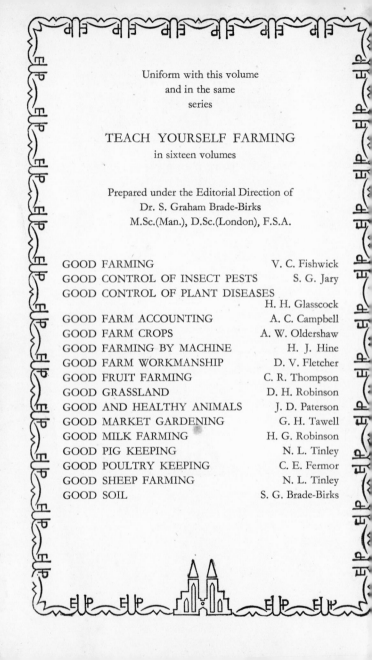

Uniform with this volume
and in the same
series

TEACH YOURSELF FARMING

in sixteen volumes

Prepared under the Editorial Direction of
Dr. S. Graham Brade-Birks
M.Sc.(Man.), D.Sc.(London), F.S.A.

GOOD FARMING	V. C. Fishwick
GOOD CONTROL OF INSECT PESTS	S. G. Jary
GOOD CONTROL OF PLANT DISEASES	
	H. H. Glasscock
GOOD FARM ACCOUNTING	A. C. Campbell
GOOD FARM CROPS	A. W. Oldershaw
GOOD FARMING BY MACHINE	H. J. Hine
GOOD FARM WORKMANSHIP	D. V. Fletcher
GOOD FRUIT FARMING	C. R. Thompson
GOOD GRASSLAND	D. H. Robinson
GOOD AND HEALTHY ANIMALS	J. D. Paterson
GOOD MARKET GARDENING	G. H. Tawell
GOOD MILK FARMING	H. G. Robinson
GOOD PIG KEEPING	N. L. Tinley
GOOD POULTRY KEEPING	C. E. Fermor
GOOD SHEEP FARMING	N. L. Tinley
GOOD SOIL	S. G. Brade-Birks

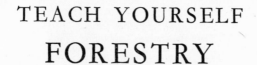

TEACH YOURSELF
FORESTRY

By

T. A. ROBBIE, B.Sc.

Chief Instructor Faskally Forester
Training School, Pitlochry,
Perthshire

ENGLISH UNIVERSITIES PRESS LTD
LONDON

Acknowledgment

The illustrations appearing on pages 60 and 62 are reproduced from *Good Soil*, by Dr. S. Graham Brade-Birks, by permission of the publishers.

First printed 1955

Made and Printed in Great Britain for The English Universities Press Ltd., London by C. Tinling & Co., Ltd., Liverpool, London and Prescot.

CONTENTS

Chapter   Page

INTRODUCTION   vii
Giving brief history of Forestry in Britain, Training
available in Forestry. Common and botanical names
of British forest trees.

I.   THE LIFE HISTORY OF A TREE . . .   I
The structure of roots, stem and crown of a tree. How
a tree grows. Photosynthesis, Respiration, Transpiration, Maturity and Reproduction.

II. SEED COLLECTION AND STORAGE . .   14
General Notes. Methods of Storage, Extraction of
Seed. Collection and Storage of conifer and hardwood
seed.

III. NURSERY WORK.   24
Selection of site. Breaking in. Preparation of seedbeds.
Sowing densities. Covering seedbeds. Weeding and
Protection of seedbeds. Stocktaking. Transplanting.
Maintenance of fertility. Vegetative propogation.

IV. PREPARATION OF GROUND FOR PLANTING .   39
Access Roads, Subdividing the area. Enclosing the
land against vermin. Preparation of ground. Preparation of soil. Drainage and ploughing forest soils.

V.   FACTORS TO BE CONSIDERED IN THE SELECTION
OF TREE SPECIES FOR PLANTING . .   58
General Considerations. The soil. Soil Types. Climatic
factors. Markets. Amenity. Pure or mixed woods.

VI. SILVICULTURAL NOTES ON THE CONIFEROUS
TREE SPECIES   69
Pines. Larches. Douglas Fir. Spruces. Silver Firs,
Hemlock Fir. Red Cedar. Cypresses.

VII. SILVICULTURAL NOTES ON THE BROADLEAVED
TREE SPECIES   80
Oaks. Beech. Sycamore. Ash. Birches. Spanish
Chestnut. Poplars. Aspen. Alder. Lime.

Chapter   Page

VIII.   PLANTING.   87
        Planting versus Natural Regeneration. Season for
        planting. Tools for Planting. Planting Methods.
        Density and control of planting. Manuring. Beating
        up. Weeding. Drain maintenance.

  IX.   TENDING AND THINNING OF PLANTATIONS   .   100
        Brashing. Cleaning. Types of Trees. Grades of
        Thinning. Marking of Thinnings. Damage during
        thinning. Thinning of Conifer species. Thinning of
        Broadleaved species. High Pruning.

   X.   MEASUREMENT   OF   FOREST   PRODUCE   AND
        STANDING CROPS   113
        Quarter Girth Volume. True Volume. Measurement
        of Round produce. Losses in conversion. Height
        measurement of a tree. Form Factor, Measurement of
        Whole Woods. Measurement of Samples. General
        Volume Tables.

  XI.   PROTECTION OF NURSERIES AND WOODLANDS   129
        Animals. Fire. Insects. Fungi.

 XII.   FELLING, EXTRACTION, CONVERSION, PRESER-
        VATION AND UTILISATION OF FOREST PRODUCE   140
        Sales of Timber. Felling. Extraction Methods. Con-
        version. Methods of Preservation. Utilisation of
        Produce.

XIII.   SURVEYING   154
        Units of Measurements. Geometrical principles.
        Instruments Ranging and Surveying. Booking of
        Survey readings. Obstacles to Chainage. Determina-
        tion of Areas. Boundaries.

        APPENDICES   172

        INDEX   179

INTRODUCTION

Every year the demand for timber or timber products increases tremendously. This has led to much greater attention being paid to forestry all over the world. Forestry is an industry, but it is also a science, the science of rearing and the tending of growing trees in order to produce the greatest income from an investment, in quality and quantity of timber. It is a science, because the student of forestry has to study nature and learn to work with nature and not to compete against nature.

In mediaeval times the word "forest" was used to convey a picture of fairly open land with trees growing on it, usually maintained for sport, and yielding some timber for fuel, house, farm and ship building. Today the word forest conveys a picture of an area of land regularly stocked with trees of varying ages and species, regularly and carefully managed to produce as much timber as the local conditions will permit.

Forestry may be subdivided into:—Arboriculture, derived from the Latin *arbor* = a tree, and means the growing and tending of individual trees such as we find on streets, in parks and open spaces; and Silviculture, derived from the Latin *sylva* = a wood, and means the growing and tending of trees in a mass such as we get in a wood or plantation.

In the Middle Ages the natural woods which covered a considerable part of Britain, were felled to provide timber for fuel and building and to clear the land for agriculture. Several Acts of Parliament were passed to try to restore and preserve the forests, but with little success. In the 18th and 19th centuries the big landowners, particularly in Scotland, invested their money by planting up large tracts of their land. As well as being an amenity, this was a source of income to their owners. During the first World War of 1914–18 a very large area of those privately owned woods were felled to provide timber for war uses. The Government of that time set up a Committee under the Chair-

manship of The Rt. Hon. F. D. Acland (known as the Acland
Committee), to investigate the possibility and organisation
required for large scale forestry in Britain. Following the
recommendations of this Committee the Government set
up the Forestry Commission, which was to receive an
annual grant of money in order to buy, lease or feu land for
growing trees, provide houses and small holdings for forest
workers and also to give advice and financial assistance to
private landowners who wished to plant trees. This scheme
worked very well until the outbreak of the second World
War in 1939. Because our ships were required to bring in
essential war materials and food, we fell back on our own
timber resources to a very great extent and a very high
proportion of our standing timber was felled, most of this
coming from the private woodland owners, as very little
of the timber owned by the state was of usable size.

At the end of hostilities other Acts of Parliament were
passed which gave the Forestry Commission more authority, and the control of its work was made the joint
responsibility of the Minister of Agriculture and Fisheries
and the Secretary of State for Scotland. The former Minister
had a particular concern for its work in England and
Wales, and the latter Minister for its work in Scotland.
Afforestation and reafforestation work carried out by the
Forestry Commission expanded on a considerable scale in
addition to that of private landowners. Financial assistance
by the state is provided under certain conditions to landowners to encourage them to plant new woodlands and to
replant the felled and derelict woodlands, to thin and
maintain their woods. Estate owners may dedicate their
lands to Forestry and thereby benefit from state assistance.
The felling of trees is controlled by felling licences, which,
in the case of clear felling, are usually granted conditional
upon the area or equivalent area being replanted.

To cope with the expansion of Forestry the Universities
where Forestry is studied increased their intake of students
to ensure that there was a supply of trained administrators

and supervisors. The Forestry Commission increased the number of their Forester Training Schools in order to provide more trained young men to supervise the actual practical operations of Forestry. More houses for workers were built and even small villages of forest workers' houses were established. Taking into consideration the work involved in planting, tending of plantations, preparation and disposal of produce and other minor allied industries, it is expected that the actual labour force engaged directly or indirectly in Forestry will, within the next fifty years, by which time it is hoped that there will be over 5,000,000 acres of forests in Britain, be in the order of some 250,000 men.

The plant kingdom is divided into many families of plants. Within a family there may be several genera, and any one genus may have several species, and each species may have several varieties. For example, the common English Pedunculate Oak is in the Family *Cupuliferae*, and in the Genus *Quercus*, and species *robur*, and is therefore botanically known as *Quercus robur*.

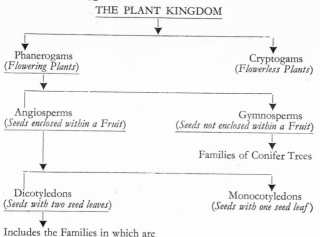

THE PLANT KINGDOM

Phanerogams
(*Flowering Plants*)

Cryptogams
(*Flowerless Plants*)

Angiosperms
(*Seeds enclosed within a Fruit*)

Gymnosperms
(*Seeds not enclosed within a Fruit*)

Families of Conifer Trees

Dicotyledons
(*Seeds with two seed leaves*)

Monocotyledons
(*Seeds with one seed leaf*)

Includes the Families in which are found the broadleaved trees.

A*

Although there are many families and species of trees which grow in this country there are very few which are grown commercially. The following are the common and botanical names of the more common forest trees in Britain. Brief botanical description of those trees may be found in Chapters six and seven.

COMMON NAME	BOTANICAL NAME
Scots Pine	*Pinus sylvestris* L.
Corsican Pine	*Pinus nigra variety calabrica* (Loud) Schneid.
Lodgepole Pine	*Pinus contorta variety latifolia* Engelm.
Mountain Pine	*Pinus mugo* Turra.
Austrian Pine	*Pinus nigra* Arnold
European Larch	*Larix decidua* Mill.
Japanese Larch	*Larix leptolepis* (Sieb. & Zucc) Murr.
Hybrid Larch	*Larix eurolepis* Henry.
Douglas Fir	*Pseudotsuga taxifolia* (Poir) Rehder.
Norway Spruce	*Picea abies* (L) Karst.
Sitka Spruce	*Picea sitchensis* (Bong) Carr.
Omorika Spruce	*Picea omorika* (Pancic) Bolle.
Common or European Silver Fir	*Abies alba* Mill.
Grand Silver Fir	*Abies grandis.*
Noble Silver Fir	*Abies nobilis.*
Hemlock Fir	*Tsuga heterophylla* (Raf). Sarg.
Red Cedar	*Thuya plicata* D. Don.
Lawson's Cypress	*Chamaecyparis lawsoniana* (A. Murr.) Parl.
Monterey Cypress	*Cupressus macrocarpa* (Hartw).
Nootka Cypress	*Chamaecyparis nootkatensis* (Lamb) Spach.
Redwood	*Sequoia sempervirens* (Lamb) Endl.
Wellingtonia	*Sequoia wellingtonia* Seem.

Broadleaved Trees.

Pedunculate Oak	*Quercus robur* L.
Sessile Oak	*Quercus petraea* (Matt). Lieblein.
Red Oak	*Quercus borealis* Mich.
Beech	*Fagus sylvatica* L.
Sycamore	*Acer pseudoplatanus* L.
Ash	*Fraxinus excelsior* L.
Birch	*Betula pubescens* Ehrh.
Silver Birch	*Betula pendula* Roth.
Spanish Chestnut	*Castanea sativa* Mill.
Black Italian Poplar	*Poulus serotina* Hartig.
Aspen	*Populus termula* L.
Common Alder	*Alnus glutinosa* Gaert.
Lime	*Tilia platyphyllos* Scop.
English Elm	*Ulmus procera* Salisb.
Wych Elm	*Ulmus glabra* Stokes.
Norway Maple	*Acer platanoides* L.
Horse Chestnut	*Aesculus hippocastanum* L.

The initial, abbreviation or name at the end of the botanical name of the trees, is that of the authority who named the tree botanically.

CHAPTER I

THE LIFE HISTORY OF A TREE

A tree may be divided into three main parts, viz:—(a) the Roots, (b) The Stem, Bole or Trunk, and (c) The Crown. Each of these parts has its various functions to perform in the life of the tree.

The Roots. Apart from providing anchorage against wind, the roots are vital to a tree as they absorb and transport some of the food materials for the growth of the tree. In early life, all young trees produce one single root going down into the soil. From this single tap-root, lateral roots are produced. From these lateral roots many subsidiary roots develop, and the younger roots are covered with fine root hairs. These hairs are extensions of the outer cells of the roots, and they absorb water from the soil. This soil water, apart from providing hydrogen and oxygen for food, has in solution, compounds of the elements essential for the growth of the tree. These elements are mainly nitrogen, potassium, phosphorus, sulphur, magnesium, calcium and iron. Other elements are generally also in the solution, although they may not be so essential for tree growth. These include chlorine, manganese, silica, boron, etc. Aluminium, although found extensively as compounds in soils, is only rarely found in the wood or foliage of trees.

The tap-root may or may not persist throughout the life of the tree, depending on the tree species and the texture and moisture content of the soil. The root system of a tree is an important feature to the forester when making his choice of species for planting on a certain site, or for special purposes, such as for shelter belts against wind. Trees can roughly be subdivided into the following categories, and the deeper rooters may generally be taken as more windfirm than the shallower rooters. Trees forming either a strong taproot or else a deep heart-shaped root system include:—Ash, Elm, Oak, Sycamore, Sweet Chestnut, Maple, Pines, Larches, Douglas Fir, and Silver Firs. Others have no persistent well developed taproot, but throw out strong side roots penetrating fairly deep into the soil, e.g., Beech Hornbeam and Aspen. Others again, like Alder, throw out strong side roots with subsidiary roots going down into the soil, while some have only a shallow root system, e.g., Spruces, Birch, Willow and Poplar.

Spruces, Lodgepole Pine, Mountain Pine, Birch, and Aspen can accommodate themselves to the least depth of soil, whilst Oak and European Larch require the greatest depth of soil. Beech, Hornbeam and Alder, although not shallow rooted, can thrive with less depth than Elm, Maple, Sycamore, Ash, Lime and Sweet Chestnut.

The Stem, Bole or Trunk. This is the most important and valuable part of the tree. Generally it is circular in cross-section but on exposed sites may develop an ovoid cross-section, with the apex facing the prevailing wind. This condition is known as "Hyponasty".

Before we go on to discuss the growth of the stem of the tree, we must first of all study the structure of that stem.

All plants are composed of cells, which are small box-like structures invisible to the naked eye, but visible under a microscope. Trees, being highly developed members of the plant kingdom, have a complex cellular structure. When first formed the cells are similar in shape, the cell walls being composed of cellulose and the contents of the cells being protoplasm with a nucleus. Soon the shape and texture of the cells become modified according to the functions which they are required to perform. The position and structure of these various types of cells are used for the identification of the various timbers.

In **Conifers,** or cone-bearing trees with needle like foliage, most of the cells become elongated to several times their width, and are called **Tracheids.** They soon lose their soft texture and become lignified and therefore woody, except for very small areas which serve as connection links between adjoining cells and are known as Pits. The tracheids are arranged in radial rows, and give strength to the tree and transport the sap from the roots to the leaves. Tracheids formed during Spring growth have comparatively thin walls and large cell cavities, whereas tracheids formed during the late summer and autumn growth have thick walls and small cell cavities, and are often flattened radially. This change in cell structure gives the very marked growth rings characteristic of conifers or softwoods.

The second important type of cell in conifers is the wood **Parenchyma,** which is a small almost rectangular cell with thin cell walls, again having pits in the wall to allow for the passage of food in solution. They retain their protoplasm. Their essential function is the storage of food. Most of the parenchyma cells are grouped in thin plates running from the centre of the tree outwards in radial direction and may be one, two or three cells thick with tracheids at the upper or lower edges.

Pits are small areas of the cell wall which have remained unthickened and so allow the passage of liquids from one cell to another. The original cell wall is left and is permeable to liquids and is called the middle lamella. The pits may be either simple or bordered as illustrated.

Ray Tracheids. Cells similar to tracheids in shape and having bordered pits, run at right angles to the vertical tracheids from the centre of the stem outwards radially and are found usually at the edge of rays which are described later.

Resin Canals. One characteristic of the coniferous trees is the secretion of resin in resin canals which run vertically up the stem of the tree, and in some cases at right angles to the stem of the tree.

In **Hardwood** or **Broadleaved** trees the structure is more complex, as the cells specialise more in their functions.

Vessels, Pores or Trachea. These are more or less cylindrical cells, placed one on top of another to form a continuous tube. They are used to conduct the sap from the roots to the leaves. This sap is allowed to pass from cell to cell in a vertical direction as the end walls are either missing or perforated. The outer walls of these cells are pitted to allow the movement of the liquids laterally. The walls of vessels are generally thickened for strength, and the most common type of thickening is spiral. The diameter of the vessels varies according to the time of the year they were formed, e.g., large in spring and smaller in summer and autumn, and they also vary with the tree species. When vessels are no longer required to conduct the sap, they become thickened and form part of the heartwood.

Fibres. These correspond to the tracheids of conifers, but act mainly for mechanical support. They form the basis of the wood and fill in the spaces round the vessels and parenchyma.

Parenchyma. These are similar to those of conifers or softwoods.

Rays. Parenchyma cells form rays running radially from the centre of the stem, but these rays are generally much thicker in hardwoods than in conifers. They can often be seen with the naked eye, and give the grain or figure to some timbers such as Oak, Beech, and Plane. Rays are used for the storage of starch as a food reserve.

In Ring Porous hardwoods the vessels formed in the spring are larger than those formed in Autumn and form a more or less definite ring. This formation is used in the identification of timbers such as Oak, Ash, Elm, etc. There is usually a distinct and sudden change in size of the vessels between spring and autumn.

Diffuse Porous hardwoods do not show this sudden change in size of vessels, and, in fact, there is very little difference in size of vessels throughout the year's growth. Examples of Diffuse Porous woods are Horse Chestnut and Willow.

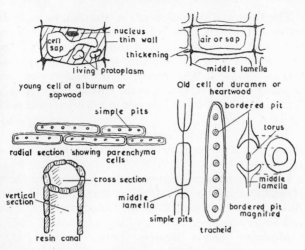

DIAGRAMMATIC ENLARGEMENT OF CELLS OF CONIFER
OR SOFTWOOD TREES

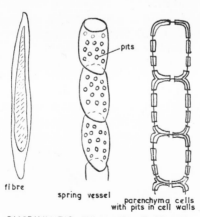

DIAGRAMMATIC ENLARGEMENT OF THE
MAIN CELLS OF BROADLEAVED OR
HARDWOOD TREES

The Crown. This consists of the branches, twigs, buds, leaves and flowers. This is a very important part of the tree, as in the leaves, the food material is absorbed and digested, and from the flowers the seed of the next generation are produced. The forester must therefore pay great attention to the development of the crown of his trees if he is to get a well developed bole, which will bring him a good financial return.

Trees vary in their demands for light or tolerance of shade for maximum growth, and may be subdivided as follows:—

Light Demanders. European Larch, Japanese Larch, Hybrid Larch, Scots Pine, Corsican Pine, Lodgepole Pine, Austrian Pine, Poplars, Willows, Oak, Ash, Elm, Alder and Sweet Chestnut.

Moderate Shade Bearers. Lime, Norway Maple, Sycamore, Weymouth Pine, Sitka Spruce and Hornbeam.

Shade Bearers. Serbian Spruce, Norway Spruce, Douglas Fir, Silver Fir, Red Cedar, Hemlock Fir, Cypress and Beech.

"Photosynthesis". The leaves or needles of the trees are the centres where the food of the tree is manufactured. The leaves take in from the air carbon dioxide gas which dissolves in the water of the leaves which has been transported from the roots. The leaves contain the green colouring matter called "Chlorophyll", which, with the action of light, a suitable temperature, and a trace of iron salt, causes carbon dioxide gas to combine with the water to form carbo-hydrates, of which sugar is the more important. As this synthetic process is dependent on light it is called "Photosynthesis."

When sugar is produced in the leaf, it is transported away downwards to act as food for other parts of the tree. When sugar is produced faster than it can be removed, a certain concentration is reached and new activities start and an insoluble starch is formed, but the action of photosynthesis can still go on. The sugar which is transported away may accumulate in other parts of the tree and starch is produced, for example, in the medullary rays, and this provides a reserve store of carbo-hydrates. When photosynthesis stops at night time the starch formerly produced in the leaves is reconverted into sugar which continues to replace the sugars withdrawn from the leaves.

The carbon-dioxide gas taken in by the leaves is made up of the two elements, Carbon and Oxygen. In photosynthesis the leaves retain most of the carbon and return most of the oxygen to the air and thus help to produce more oxygen for human beings to breathe.

Respiration. In addition to the process of photosynthesis which is taking place in the leaves, a tree must also breathe in air, retaining part of the oxygen and exhaling carbon dioxide gas. This process of respiration is the exact opposite of Photosynthesis, and they can be compared as follows:—

Photosynthesis.	*Respiration.*
1. Is a feeding process.	1. Is a breathing process.
2. Carbon dioxide gas is retained.	2. Carbon dioxide gas is returned to the air.
3. Oxygen is returned to the air.	3. Oxygen is retained.
4. Purifies the air.	4. Fouls the air.
5. Only takes place in green parts.	5. Takes place in all parts.
6. Only takes place in sunlight.	6. Goes on day and night.

During the day Photosynthesis is more active, and more oxygen is returned to the air than is retained. At night, of course, Respiration only takes place, but over the whole twenty-four hours more oxygen is produced than carbon dioxide, and thus the air is made purer.

Air comes into a tree and gases pass out from a tree mainly from minute openings on the skin of the leaf or needles, and these openings called Stomata, are found mostly on the underside of leaves. They are not visible to the naked eye. In addition to these stomata or breathing pores of the leaves, there are pores in the bark of trees which are used for breathing purposes. These are called Lenticels. They are only visible on smooth barked trees such as Birch, Hazel, Cherry, etc., but they are in fact present on rough barked trees.

Transpiration. We have seen that water, containing very small quantities of minerals in solution, is transported from the roots up the stem of the tree to the leaves. A very large amount of water must pass through the tree in order that it may have a sufficient supply of minerals. A very small quantity of this water is used to transport the sugars from the leaves down the stem of the tree and to form the liquid part of the cells as they are produced. The excess water must go somewhere, and it is evaporated into the air through the stomata. This evaporation from the leaves is called Transpiration. On a hot day transpiration from the leaves is rapid, and if the soil immediately surrounding these roots becomes dry so that the roots do not get sufficient water, slight wilting of the leaves may take place. The water from the soil is pumped upwards through the stem of the tree by an osmotic pressure, or Osmosis, and partly by the action of Transpiration.

How a Tree Grows. There are two types of growth in a tree which are going on at the same time, (a) Height Growth, and (b) Growth in Girth. The combined growth giving Volume.

Height Growth. Trees consist mainly of a leading shoot which later in life thickens to become the bole of the tree. At the end of the leading shoot there is found in winter a terminal bud, usually surrounded by a varying number of lateral, or side buds. In spring, when growth starts, the terminal bud increases by forming new cells growing mainly upwards, putting on a very thin layer of cells laterally, and forming needles or leaves as it grows. The lateral buds develop sideways, and send out needles and leaves as they grow. These lateral shoots finish growth at the end of the growing season by the formation of a central bud with a few side buds, so that each year the number of side branches, thus the number of twigs, increases. If trees are allowed to grow in the open they will retain their living branches and twigs for many years. If trees are grown closely the branches of adjoining trees soon interlace, and exclude light from one another, and therefore stop the process of Photosynthesis. This results in the death of lower twigs and branches. The forester must therefore carefully watch the development of the crowns of his trees, in order that lower branches will be killed off so that more valuable knot-free growth is put on, and also that there is sufficient live crown to produce food for the continuing growth of the tree.

The growth of the leading shoot is much quicker than the growth of the side shoots, as there is more direct light and a greater intensity of light concentrated on the top of the tree.

Growth in Girth. As the tree grows in height, in order that it may stand up to the force of the wind and to its own weight, it must grow in girth also. The food which is formed in the leaves and not required for the upward or side growth of branches, is transported down the stem and helps to produce the cells to make the growth in girth. If the cross-section of the stem, trunk or bole of the tree is magnified, we find a thin layer of living cells between the bark and the wood. This layer of cells is called the Cambium. When growth starts in the Spring, this cambial layer, receiving food from the sugary sap coming down from the leaves, produces more cells. Those produced on its inner side form wood cells, and on its outer bark cells. Many more wood cells are produced than bark cells, thus the layer of wood is much thicker than that of bark. In this way each year a layer of wood is added to the outside of the older wood, and a new layer of bark to the inner side of the old bark. The result of this is that the outer bark, which has died off, becomes stretched until it can stretch no more, and cracks or peels off. Before this stage is reached another layer of cells is put on from a cork cambium layer, so that the tree is always protected by a layer of cork. Between the cork cambium and the wood cambium is a living layer of inner bark or *Bast* down which the food material passes from the leaves to any part of the living cambium of the tree.

In spring the new wood cells produced are larger to take the sap from the roots to the leaves, but by autumn as the sap flow is falling off the cells made by the cambium are smaller. This gives rise to the difference in texture in wood and to the appearance of annual rings in the cross-section of the bole of the tree. The amount of wood laid on each year depends on the amount of food available, and this in turn depends on the amount of root and crown room available to trees. Foresters therefore can control the amount of wood laid on each year by the growing space which they allow the trees in a plantation. This is discussed further under the heading of Thinning of Woodlands.

Minerals form a very small part of the composition of the wood of a tree, as is shown by the small amount of ash that remains on burning—probably about 1 per cent of the weight. The greater part of the wood is organic matter, apart from the water contained in the cells. In fairly young wood cells, the most important constituents are cellulose and semi-cellulose, which are derived from the sugars made in the leaves. It is the presence of these constituents that make timber so valuable for the pulp, paper, rayon and explosives industries.

As the layers of the new wood cells are laid on each year by the cambium, the older layers of cells are not required for conducting water to the leaves of the tree and the protoplasm of the cell usually dies off and the cell walls harden. This is due to the presence of lignin, whose function is mainly to act as a cement holding the individual cells together as a mechanical reinforcement of the cellulose. Woods of high lignin content are usually of high compressive strength. Lignin can be isolated from timber and is used in the preparation of car batteries and plastic mouldings.

When the layers of cells have become lignified, they sometimes change colour, to a deeper red or brown, readily visible in the cross-section, and this is known as the heartwood or duramen. The living cells not yet lignified form the sapwood or alburnum. The heartwood, especially of some of the hardwood trees, has a much greater strength and durability than the sapwood.

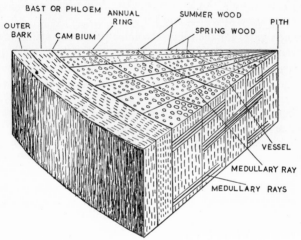

DIAGRAMMATIC CROSS SECTION OF A FIVE YEAR OLD
BROADLEAVED TREE

Growth in Volume. Tree species vary considerably in their rate of height growth, which is not influenced by the density of stocking of trees on the ground. They also vary considerably in their rate of girth growth, but this growth is influenced by the density of stocking on the ground, and can be affected by the way in which a forester thins his woods. The same tree species varies in its rate of growth depending on the site in which it is grown. In a site suitable for a species, with soil, climate and topography favourable, the volume production is at its best, and such a site is called the optimum site for that tree species.

In the same period of years, the following list gives the common tree species in sequence from greatest volume producers to least volume producers.

(a) **Conifers.** *Abies grandis*, Sitka Spruce, *Abies nobilis*, Douglas Fir, Norway Spruce, Hybrid Larch, Japanese Larch, Red Cedar, European Larch, Hemlock Fir, Corsican Pine, Scots Pine and Lodgepole Pine.

(b) **Hardwoods.** Poplar, Beech, Oak, Ash, Elm, Sycamore, Maple, Sweet Chestnut and Lime.

Some figures for the biggest volume producing stands are given in Appendix 2.

Maturity and Longevity. If trees were allowed to grow without being felled, there is every reason to believe that they would live for a very long time. Records are always being produced as to the oldest trees of each species, but where trees are grown for the economic production of timber, there is an age beyond which the growth in volume is so small as not to justify keeping the trees growing any longer. This may be brought about by the dying off of roots or dying off of crown. For some of our more common tree species the longest economic age on better quality sites may be approximately as follows:—

Larch, Scots Pine and Spruces .... 80 years
Douglas Fir, Silver Firs, etc.................... 90 years
Willow, Birch, Poplars .... 60 years
Ash, Elm, Maple, Sycamore .... 70–80 years
Beech....................................... 90–120 years
Oak ....120–150 years

Reproduction. At some stage in their lifetime most trees bear flowers. These flowers may have both male and female organs in the one flower, or have separate male and female flowers on the one tree, or have trees bearing male flowers only and trees bearing female flowers only. The time at which trees begin to bear flowers varies tremendously according to species and site conditions. Trees have certain qualities inherited from their parents and one of these qualities may be the ability to bear seed.

The ability to form seed depends on the amount of starchy and nitrogenous reserves secreted in the tree, and this of course varies according to its age, the soil and situation, and the amount of light and heat which the tree has. The most prolific period of seed production is when the trees have completed their main height growth and have begun to expand their crowns, because that is the time when their vital energy is greatest. Good soil, warm situation and a free growing space favour the production of seed. In a forest, generally, the flowering and production of fertile seed starts at:—

15 to 20 years old for Pines, Larches, Birch and Alder
20 to 25   ,,   ,,   ,, Douglas Fir.
25 to 30   ,,   ,,   ,, Sitka Spruce.
30 to 40   ,,   ,,   ,, Norway Spruce, Ash, Elm,
                           Maple, Hornbeam, Sycamore.
40 to 50   ,,   ,,   ,, Beech and Oak.
50 to 60   ,,   ,,   ,, Silver Firs.

It is a fact that if a tree is checked by any cause it will tend to produce more seed, and again when reaching maturity. Seed years or mast years are years in which trees produce a rich harvest of seed, and these do not occur every year, but periodically. In the case of Beech a full mast year occurs generally every ten years, with a partial mast year every three to five years. In Oak a full mast year occurs every five to six years, with a partial mast every two to three years. This is due to the fact that the formation of fruit exhausts the reserve materials and only when the storage cells have been replenished is the full formation of fruit again possible.

Apart from reproduction by seed, trees may be propagated by other means, such as stool shoots, root suckers, etc. This is dealt with in the next chapter.

CHAPTER II

SEED COLLECTION AND STORAGE

Trees may be propagated from seed or by cuttings, layers, grafts, stool shoots, or from root suckers. Small land owners may not wish or may not have the ground to establish a small nursery, but if land is available the rearing of trees is a fascinating job, and has the added advantage of being cheaper than the purchase of young trees for planting. Other owners who do not wish to raise trees from seed may buy seedlings from a nurseryman and transplant them in their own land so that they are available as desired for planting in the forest.

Several points must be borne in mind before seed is collected. The most important is that generally the characteristics of the parent tree are found in the seedling, therefore care must be taken to select seed only from good type trees. Rough, heavily branched, twisting trees should be avoided. Seed or cones should not be collected from too young, immature trees as these undesirable characteristics may not have shown themselves. The time of flushing of leaves of the parent trees is also an important point, e.g., if plants are required for a cold site, seed from trees which are naturally late flushing will ensure that there is less risk of damage from late Spring frosts. The other important point to bear in mind is the time at which the seed ripens and falls to the ground. This point is dealt with later for each species.

Trees do not necessarily produce seed every year, because of the reserve of food which is used up in producing seed. Good seed years are known as "mast" years. It may be necessary therefore to collect more seed in a good mast year than is required immediately, as an insurance against non-production the following year, and this seed stored until required. Some seeds will keep in storage for a year or two but many do not and it may then be necessary to sow and try to keep the plants growing longer before planting out.

If seed is being purchased from a seed merchant care should be taken to find out the source of seed before purchase is agreed. It may be found that the seed is from a race, strain or provenance which is unsuited to the locality. Germination percentage and purity of the seed offered should also be investigated.

It is not often that one is able to collect seed or cones from trees which are being felled. As climbing, or use of climbing equipment in order to collect seed or cones is difficult and expensive, it is wisest to collect small samples of cones and cut them open by knife, to test if there are enough sound seed to justify collection, before a great deal of money is spent on collecting useless cones. Only cones which have ripened during the current year should be collected, as after the first year the cones will have opened and the seed fallen out.

To avoid climbing trees to collect seed, the Forestry Commission and some private landowners in this country as well as authorities abroad, have started tree orchards. Ordinary stock is planted at fairly wide spacing, and after establishment, scions of the same species collected from the top branches of élite trees are grafted on to these stock trees. These top branches are at the fruit and seed bearing stage and when grafted to short trees will produce fruit and cones much nearer the ground, and therefore make seed collection much easier.

There are several methods of dealing with seed after collection, such as (a) sowing immediately, (b) storing dry in glass carboys, (c) stratifying, and (d) storing fresh in pits or sheds.

(a) This method is self-explanatory.

(b) The seeds are air dried, to prevent moulding later,

before being put into glass jars for small quantities, or carboys for larger quantities. The jars or carboys should be corked and sealed with wax.

(c) Stratifying Pits are pits dug into the ground. The bottom of the pit is filled with good drainage material such as stones, cinders or gravel, leaving a depth of pit about two feet, and two feet wide, and of length as required. The pits should be lined with mouse-proof netting wire. The seed, having been tested for germination, is weighed out in small amounts say $\frac{1}{2}$lb or 1lb lots, then mixed with clean sharp sand, and each lot put in a separately partitioned section of the pit. On top of the seed and sand mixture is put a layer of mouse-proof netting, then pure sand about 3 inches to 6 inches deep, and on top of this the soil is replaced. This stratification keeps the seed moist, softens the seed coat, and increases and hastens the germination of the seed when sown.

(d) Some seed is moist when collected and should be spread out to allow the seed coats to dry, and turned during this process. Shallow pits about 18 inches deep may be dug in the soil, and the sides lined with mouse wire-netting. The pits should be well drained. The seed can be placed in these pits to a depth of about 12 inches, and turned regularly. The pit should be protected by a roof. If the seeds are stored in a barn they may dry out too much and may require to be slightly moistened. They can be protected from vermin by spraying with paraffin.

Extraction of Seed. Some of the cones of the conifer species require heating to make them open to allow the seeds to fall out. No elaborate system is required for this, and anyone with a heated greenhouse can treat all species except European Larch. Larch, in addition to heating, requires to be put through a crushing or husking machine. Details for each species are given later.

Labelling of Seed. When seed has been collected or

bought and put in storage it should be given some label of identity, so that its history may always be traced. This identity should give its year of collection and source of origin.

Collection of Seed of Individual Species.

Conifers.

Scots Pine. Select seed trees of good stem form and height growth. Collect cones after first frosts, mid-December to March. Heat to about 100°F. for 7 hours until cones open and seed falls out. Put seed through winnowing machine to clean from seed wing. Store dry. 1 Bushel of cones yields approximately 6 ozs. of seed.

Corsican Pine. Most seed imported as few mature trees yet in Britain. Must ensure that strain is suitable, avoiding the Ursuline strain. Collect cones from December to March. Heat to about 100°F. for 6 hours. Clean seed, store dry. 1 Bushel of cones might yield 6 ozs of seed.

Lodgepole Pine. Mainly imported as few mature trees yet in Britain. If mature trees of true strain available cones can be collected November to February and treated as for Scots Pine, including storage, up to a certain time. The seed should be stratified for six to eight weeks before sowing. 1 Bushel of cones might yield about 4 ozs of seed.

Other Pines. May be treated similarly to Scots Pine.

European Larch. Home seed best, particularly from Morayshire or Perthshire strain. Collected from October to January. Heat and put through husking machine if dealing with large quantities. Bushel of cones will give about 14 ozs of seed. Store dry.

Japanese Larch. Cones often open early and close watch must be kept to collect immediately after ripening. Much seed imported. Select parent trees carefully as many trees are inclined to twist and spiral growth. Collect October–November. Heat and extract. Store dry. Bushel of cones gives about 10 ozs seed.

Hybrid Larch. Not many plantations at seed-bearing age. Demand exceeds supply. Mostly bought through trade.

CONES

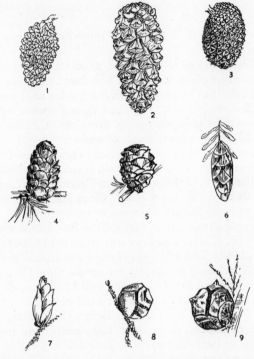

1— SCOTS PINE   4— EUROPEAN LARCH   7— RED CEDAR

2—CORSICAN PINE   5—JAPANESE LARCH   8—LAWSON'S CYPRESS

3 — LODGEPOLE PINE   6—HEMLOCK FIR   9—MONTEREY CYPRESS

CONES

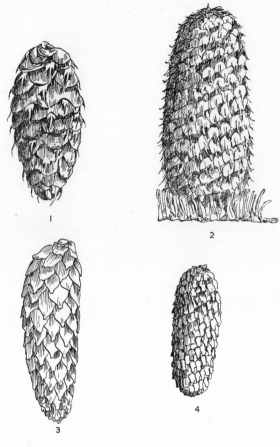

1 — DOUGLAS FIR

2 — NOBLE SILVER FIR

3 — NORWAY SPRUCE

4 — SITKA SPRUCE

All true hybrid trees should be selected as parents. Collect cones October–November. Heat and store dry.

Douglas Fir. Mostly imported seed. Seed liable to attack by Seed Fly (*Megastigmus spermotrophus*). Do not collect from Blue or Grey varieties. Collect October–November. Heat and extract seed. Store dry but stratify 8–10 weeks before sowing.

Norway Spruce. Mostly home collection. Seed liable to attack by Megastigmus. Collect October–early December. Heat and extract seed. Store dry. Bushel of cones gives about 16 ozs seed.

Sitka Spruce. Home collections now good, but much imported. Select good type trees, not twisted or rough branched. Cones ripen early. Collection may be made end of September to early November. Watch must be kept for ripening. Slight heat, extract, store dry. Bushel of cones gives 16 ozs seed.

Omorika Spruce or Serbian Spruce. Seed scarce and cones should be collected from all available trees. Collect October–November. Heat, extract and store dry.

Silver Firs (all species). Cones ripen early and soon fall apart. Collection must be made before cones break up. Seed mainly imported. Cones will break up and seed must be separated from scales. Store dry or sow immediately and protect against frost.

Hemlock Fir. Mostly imported, but home collection should be made if available. Cones ripen early and should be collected about end of September. Slight heat opens cones. Store dry.

Cypresses and Cedar. Cones of both genera ripen early and collection should be made about end of September. Slight heat will extract seed. Store dry except with Nootka Cypress which requires to be stratified for one year before sowing.

Sequoia Species. Difficult to grow from home seed as mostly infertile but sempervirens may be worth collecting. Not planted much as forest trees, but mainly for amenity.

BROADLEAVED SEEDS

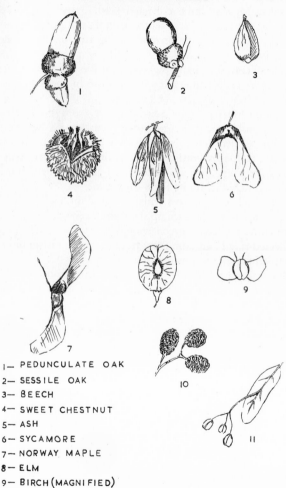

1— PEDUNCULATE OAK
2— SESSILE OAK
3— BEECH
4— SWEET CHESTNUT
5— ASH
6— SYCAMORE
7— NORWAY MAPLE
8— ELM
9— BIRCH (MAGNIFIED)
10— ALDER (FALSE CONES).
11— LIME

Broadleaved Trees.

Oaks. Mostly home collected seed. Select good type trees for collection. First acorns to fall are usually empty, but should be tested. Ground under tree can be swept about early October and when ripe brown acorns fall they can be swept up or hand picked about the end of October. Mast years at infrequent intervals. Store in sheds keeping moist, or in pits as described earlier.

Beech. Mostly home seed. Collect from good clean straight boled trees, avoid fluted stem type. Mast years variable. Collect from ground as for Oak, but ensure that seed are fertile by cutting before collection. Collect October–November. Store on floors until January then stratify in moderately damp pits for 8–10 weeks.

Ash. Collect from trees which are straight, clean and not forking for some distance up the stem. Seed produced very frequently. Collected green should be sown immediately. Collected ripe in autumn from trees or ground it should be stratified for 18 months before sowing.

Sycamore and Maple. Collect seed from good, straight boled, less branching type of tree. Seed usually produced each year, and ripens in autumn. Collect from ground after seeds have fallen. Store in moist sand until spring, or store dry.

Sweet or Spanish Chestnut. Not planted on any very large scale. May be grown from stool shoots after felling. Seed ripens only in South of England. Collect from ground end of October–November. Store dry or stratify until spring.

Birch. Select from well-grown trees. Silver Birch for preference. Fertile seed usually produced every year. Catkins ripen quickly about end of September and quickly break up. Collect branches of catkins when nearly ripe and allow seed to fall off. Store dry until January then stratify for 10–12 weeks. Not much grown for planting.

Alder. Cone-like woody seed bearing structures are picked from trees in November–December. Gentle heat releases seed. Store seed dry and stratify for 6–8 weeks before sowing.

Lime. Collect seed from trees or from ground in October. Stratify for 18 months before sowing. Lime is usually grown from root suckers or stool shoots.

Elm. Gather seed in early summer as it falls from tree before it scatters, or from tree just on ripening. Should be sown immediately and seedbeds covered with sand, and watered until seed germinates.

Horse Chestnut. Not planted as a forest tree. Collect fruit when ripe in September–October. Store in pits.

Poplars (except Aspen). As most varieties are hybrids which do not breed true from seed, Poplars are nearly always raised from cuttings, which strike very readily.

Aspen. Collect seed from tree when ripe in early summer (May). This stage of ripeness is indicated by the woolliness of the fruiting branches. Separate seed from woolly wings. Sow immediately as seed does not keep more than a week. Seedbeds must be watered and kept continually moist until seedlings are well through. Seedbeds must be protected against wind, rain and strong sunshine.

CHAPTER III

NURSERY WORK

Selection of Site for Nursery.

If it is desired to start a new nursery consideration must be given to certain factors in selecting the site.

Size. This will entirely depend on the quantities of plants it is intended to produce, but the nursery should be sited so that it may be enlarged if necessary.

Soil. A good deep soil, slightly acid in reaction, is preferable. Shallow, or heavy soils should where possible be avoided. Light, sandy soils may be used as they can be improved. Heavy soils are inclined to give "frost lift"— described later.

Exposure. Choose, if possible, a fairly sheltered site, but not one in which frost may lie, causing damage to young plants.

Aspect. Northerly aspect is probably best as there is less risk of damage by early sun on frozen plants.

Access. Near to a good road for delivery of manures, seedbed covering material and despatch of plants. Close to a supervisor's house if possible.

Water Supply. Near to water supply in case watering of seedbeds may be necessary.

Drainage. Preferably on a slight slope to ensure good natural, or if necessary, artificial drainage.

Shape. Does not matter very much, but nearly rectangular or square in preference to irregular shaped piece of ground, mainly for economy of fencing.

Layout and Breaking-in of Nursery. Having selected the site, the area must be enclosed by a good stock and rabbit-proof fence (details described later under Fencing), and the area cleared of rabbits. Protecting perimeter hedges may require to be established. One of the best hedging plants is Beech, but this may grow slowly in places, and it may be best to establish an evergreen hedge such as Cypress. Field tile drains may have to be laid where necessary. The area should be laid off in sections of good working size, rectangular or square, with subsidiary roads or paths across it. Size of sections will depend mainly on whether mechanical equipment is to be used. If grassland has been chosen it should be well ploughed and a crop of potatoes taken off. This will help to clear weeds by cultivation. It is not generally recommended that seed should be sown on freshly broken-in land, but this can be done. Some people prefer to put in a crop of plants, in transplant lines which have been brought in. If transplant lines are used first the ground is more easily kept clean. It must be borne in mind that if soil fertility is to be maintained a proper rotation must be followed, e.g. 1/4 fallow or greencrop, 1/4 seedbeds and 1/2 area in transplant lines (approximately).

Preparation of Seedbeds. The land for seedbeds should be thoroughly cultivated by hand or mechanically by plough, Rotovator or Rotary Hoe, so that a good tilth is made for at least six inches deep. On heavy ground and in high rainfall areas the seedbeds should be from 4 inches to six inches above the paths between the beds. The beds are laid out 3 feet 6 inches wide with an alley or path of 1 foot 6 inches between beds. The beds may be thrown up by plough or on a small scale by hand. A light application of a general fertiliser may be applied and worked into the beds. The soil may be sterilised by the application of formalin solution, but this must be done at least three weeks before seed sowing. Immediately prior to seed sowing the surface of the beds should be raked over. In localities where the soil is light it may be preferred to put a light hand-drawn wooden roller over the beds before sowing. This gives a more even surface for seed sowing.

Methods of Sowing. Drill, Band and Broadcast

Drill Sowing. In areas where weed growth may be expected, and where it may be possible to use mechanical means to kill the weeds, drill sowing is preferred. A wooden roller with slats or laths nailed along at about 4 inch spacing, is drawn along the seedbed thus leaving small drills of the depth required for seed sowing. The seed is sown from a lath to give the correct density, and covered with sand, grit or loam to the correct depth. The beds are lightly rolled.

Band Sowing. For some of the hardwoods such as Oak or Beech, shallow trenches or bands about 6 inches wide are taken out of the soil, and seed sown in these tracks. The soil is raked back to cover the seed to the proper depth. (See table opposite).

Broadcast Sowing. In this method the seed may be scattered evenly over the surface of the seedbed by hand or by machine. In drill and broadcast sowing only 3 feet of the bed must be covered, thus preventing loss of seedlings from the edges of the bed. Only the correct density of sowing must be made, and the correct depth of cover.

Testing of Seed. Seed must be tested in order that the area required for sowing can be determined. They can be tested by taking 100 seeds and cutting with a knife to find the percentage of fertile seed; or by setting 100 seeds on moist flannel or blotting paper and counting the number which germinate. Seed testing should be done whilst the bulk is in store, and some time before sowing takes place.

Sowing Densities. The following table gives the standard densities usually adopted for sowing seed of normal germination.

Species	Square yards per lb of seed		Normal % germination	Depth of cover in inches	Average No. seeds per lb.
	Drills	*Broadcast*			
Scots Pine	75	55	90	$\frac{1}{4}$	75,000
Corsican Pine	50	35	55	$\frac{3}{8}$	32,000
Lodgepole Pine	90	75	90	$\frac{1}{4}$	140,000
Mountain Pine	20	15	25	$\frac{1}{4}$	25,000
Austrian Pine	50	35	65	$\frac{3}{8}$	25,000
European Larch	65	55	50	$\frac{1}{8}$	70,000
Japanese Larch	80	60	50	$\frac{1}{8}$	90,000
Hybrid Larch	80	60	50	$\frac{1}{8}$	90,000
Douglas Fir	60	45	80	$\frac{1}{4}$	40,000
Norway Spruce	60	45	85	$\frac{1}{4}$	60,000
Sitka Spruce	115	85	90	$\frac{1}{8}$	190,000
Omorika Spruce	60	45	90	$\frac{1}{4}$	60,000
European Silver Fir	40	30	50	$\frac{3}{8}$	10,000
Grand Silver Fir	30	25	35	$\frac{3}{8}$	10,000
Noble Fir	30	25	35	$\frac{3}{8}$	15,000
Hemlock Fir	90	60	60	$\frac{1}{8}$	300,000
Red Cedar	60	45	65	$\frac{1}{8}$	340,000
Lawson's Cypress	55	40	45	$\frac{1}{8}$	180,000
Monterey Cypress	40	25	35	$\frac{1}{4}$	73,000
Redwood	20	15	15	$\frac{1}{8}$	100,000
Wellingtonia	20	15	15	$\frac{1}{8}$	100,000

Broadleaved Trees

Species	Square yards per lb. of seed		Normal % germination	Depth of cover in inches	Average No. seeds per lb.
	6" wide Bands	*Broadcast*			
	Running yards per lb of Seed				
Oak	$2\frac{1}{2}$	1	75	1	120
Beech	10	4	35	$\frac{3}{4}$	2,000
Sycamore	25	10	55	$\frac{1}{2}$	5,000
Ash	30	12	50	$\frac{1}{2}$	6,000
Birch	—	30	20	$\frac{1}{8}$	600,000
Sweet Chestnut	$2\frac{1}{2}$	1	70	1	100–120
Alder	—	30	30	$\frac{1}{8}$	200,000
Lime	—	14	30	$\frac{1}{2}$	10,000
Elm	—	6	40	$\frac{1}{8}$	40,000
Maple	25	10	55	$\frac{1}{2}$	5,000
Horse Chestnut	4	1	20–25	1	80–100

For example, one pound of Scots Pine seed to be sown broadcast has, on being tested, a germination of 60 per cent. It is desired to find the area required for sowing this seed. From the foregoing table it will be seen that for one pound of seed of 90 per cent germination 55 square yards are required. Therefore the area required for 60 per cent germination

$$\frac{55}{90} \times \frac{60}{1} = 36\frac{2}{3} \text{ square yards.}$$

Preparation of Conifer Seed for Sowing. Apart from Douglas Fir and Lodgepole Pine which are weighed out in small lots before stratifying, the seed of other conifers is usually weighed out in small lots (usually enough for one bed) put in a small bag and soaked in water for 12–24 hours to soften the seed coat. The seed is then spread to dry and when nearly dry is given a fine dusting of red lead, (about one pound red lead to ten pounds seed). This is added mainly so that the seed may be visible when sowing. Formerly red lead used to be considered a deterrent to mice and birds from eating the seeds.

Covering Material for Seedbeds. Normal seedbed soil may be quite suitable for covering the seeds and can be raked or riddled on to the correct depth. It has, however, been found that covering by sand or lime-free grit has prevented the surface from caking, retained a certain amount of surface moisture and therefore produced a better germination. This covering may be applied by riddling on by hand or by a mechanical grit distributor. Depth of covering must be strictly watched.

Seedbed Soil Acidity. It has been found that conifer seedlings do not flourish in soils which contain too high a lime content, or are basic in reaction. Even some broad-leaved seedlings appear to do better in soil which is slightly acid. Scientists have produced a chart of soil acidity, and in this chart 7·2 is classed as neutral and the table may be shown for forestry purposes as:—

3·5 = Extremely acid
4·5 = Very acid
5·6 = Moderately acid
6·5 = Slightly acid
7·2 = Neutral
8·0 = Alkaline

These numbers are known as pH values.

If possible conifer seed should be sown in soil with acidity between 5·6 and 7·0, and most broadleaved seed in slightly acid soil. It is not easy to acidify soil, but this may be done by the addition of peat, or of sulphur, or the soil may be sterilised by formalin solution.

Weeding Seedbeds. Many young seedlings may be pulled out of the seedbeds if weeding is done by hand, and handweeding is a very expensive operation. Therefore, anything that can be done to reduce this cost should be tried. Sterilisation of soil by formalin some three weeks before sowing will reduce weeds. Burning of weeds before seedlings appear above ground by a type of hand flame thrower, (usually a Hauck Gun) is successful. The application of an oil spray before emergence of tree seedlings is effective on weeds, but care must be taken that the solution is not too strong, or too heavy an application. T.V.O. applied before emergence of tree seedlings and White Spirits applied after emergence of tree seedlings up to eight weeks, should be applied as a fine mist in cool weather. A reliable spray must be used.

In broadcast sowing, hand weeding must be done after all these other methods have been tried. With drill and band sowing narrow hand hoes can be used, and even mechanical hoes may be used. Weeds should be picked before they seed and may be composted. Some people will on no account put composted weeds back on their land. Others burn their weeds in incinerators and return the ash to the soil on the greencrop area.

Time required for Seed to Germinate. Most Conifers

B*

require about three weeks before they germinate. Sitka Spruce may require four weeks. Douglas Fir and Lodgepole Pine may not require this length of time if they have been stratified and sowing held up by wet weather. Time to germinate will be lengthened if dry weather prevails after sowing, but if possible watering of seedbeds should be avoided, as once started, watering should continue until the seedlings are through the ground. If watering is to be done do it in late afternoon or early evening.

Broadleaved trees vary considerably with species and locality, but generally take two to three weeks before they show above ground.

Protection of Seedbeds

(a) **Scorch, Frost and Wind.** Seedlings, when they first germinate, send up cotyledons or seed leaves. These are very tender, and in the South where there may be high temperatures in May the seedlings need protection from scorch. Certain conifers, particularly in their first year, require protection from severe frosts and especially against early and very late frosts. The species normally protected are all conifers except Scots Pine, European Larch and Norway Spruce, and most of the broadleaved species are covered in Scotland. The shelter provided may be of two types, (1) Wooden laths (as formerly used by plasterers) are wired to old cable at about one inch spacing across two or three cables. This forms a type of venetian blind which can be rolled up easily. Stakes are driven in at the side of seedbeds and fencing wire stretched on these stakes about one foot from the ground. The lath shelter is rolled out on top of these wires in time of frost, either early or late. (2) In high rainfall areas the lath-type shelter is inclined to cause damage by drips falling on the seedbeds. In place of lath shelters, green branches are stuck into the ground on the south side of the bed and made to lean over the seedbeds. Wires are fixed for the branches to lean on, and the branches are held in position by another wire.

(b) **Frost Lift.** When water freezes it expands. When the water in soil freezes it expands and can only expand upwards. If young seedlings are rooted in the soil then these are pulled up when the soil freezes. When the frozen soil moisture melts, the soil contracts and leaves the seedlings on the surface of the beds, their roots dry out and the seedlings die. Frost lift is worst on heavy and moisture holding soils, therefore to reduce or prevent frost lift the soil must be treated first by:—(1) Efficient drainage of seedbeds, (2) Maintaining high humus content in the soil and (3) Keeping seedbeds on those sections which are less susceptible. Every effort to avoid frost lift should be made, by maintaining good fertility and sowing as early as possible to get vigorous and strong-rooted plants before frost sets in. Before frost is expected, sand, or a mixture of peat and sand, or leaf mould and sand, should be sprinkled over the seedbeds partially burying the seedlings. If the seedlings are partially lifted by frost, there is much more chance of survival if this is done.

(c) **Wind.** Where the soil is light and sandy it may be necessary to prevent the wind blowing off surface soil in a very dry spring. In this case boards six inches to eight inches deep should be set on their edge along the sides of the seed beds.

Labelling of Seedbeds. It is essential that parcels of seeds should be identified and traced at all stages, therefore seedbeds should be clearly labelled immediately after sowing.

Stocktaking. Near the end of the growing season (about August) it is necessary to check the heights and numbers of plants in the seedbed, so that the owner may decide what to do with the seedlings, according to size and numbers. A percentage count of stock, normally 10 per cent is sufficient. Frames are made with wooden ends, six inches long, with wires for sides as wide as the seedbeds. If these wire frames are laid across the seedbed at five foot intervals and all seedlings counted within the frame, this will give the

10 per cent stocktaking required. Following stocktaking
the owner may decide to (a) leave seedlings for another
year in the seedbeds, (b) undercut the seedlings, (c) transplant the seedlings (d) use the seedlings to plant out in the
forest.

Undercutting of Seedlings. If seedlings are to be kept
for another year in the seedbeds they would develop very
strong straggly roots. If the main tap root of seedlings is
cut about four to six inches underground, depending on
depth of rooting, they will develop a fine fibrous root
system, similar to those of a transplant, but without the
cost of transplanting. On large scale work undercutting is
done by a blade pulled through the soil by tractor. On a
small scale the same effects can be achieved by cutting at
an angle under the seedlings with a spade, or wrenching the
seedlings with a fork. This wrenching is done by inserting
the fork under the seedling roots and pressing quickly
down on the handle. This wrenches up the plant, thus
breaking the main tap root.

Lifting, Grading and Transplanting of Seedlings.
This is sometimes called "lining-out" or "bedding."
Transplanting is done in order to give seedlings more room
to develop their roots and shoots. It is normally carried out
when plants are dormant. Seedlings are loosened either by
machine or by men with forks or spades. The seedlings are
then lifted from the soil and put into boxes so that their
roots are not exposed and allowed to dry out. The seedlings
are graded in a shed, according to size, usually two sizes.
Weak, forked or poor specimens are cast aside as culls.
There are several variations of transplanting; on a small
scale may be done by hand, on a bigger scale using transplanting boards and turning over the soil by spade, and on
a very large scale by using transplanting boards and turning
over the soil by plough.

(a) **Transplanting by hand.** The soil at one side of a
section of the nursery is turned up one spit wide and
levelled by the back of the spade. A vertical face about eight

to ten inches deep is then cut along the levelled spit. The seedlings are held, one at a time, against this cut face so that their roots hang freely in the trench and the plants are about one and a half inches apart. A little soil is pulled by hand on to their roots and holds them in position. Another spit width is dug against this row of plants, firmed by foot into the roots and levelled. A line is then set about ten inches from the first row and a trench cut for the next row.

This continues so that we get our seedlings transplanted one and a half inches apart in the rows with ten inches between the rows. This allows free hand-weeding, hoeing and mechanical hoeing between the rows.

(b) **Using Transplanting or Lining-out Boards.** A lining-out board is a device for holding seedlings in position whilst they are being transplanted. The boards are usually six to ten feet long. They consist of two boards about four inches wide and half an inch thick hinged together by metal straps. Attached by chain to the top board is a clamping ring. On the inner faces of these two boards is attached draught rubber tubing or sorbo rubber to prevent damage to the plants when the boards are closed. The boards, opened out, are laid singly across trestles at about waist level. Against the edge of the lower board is placed a master board with notches in it at the spacing required for the transplants. The plants are placed singly in these notches so that the mark of where they were in the ground as seedlings is at the junction of the masterboard and lower board. When all the notches are filled the top board is brought over and clamped down. The full transplanting board is then carried to the face which has been cut by spade for transplanting. The board is set on the level surface and is held by a pin through a metal band which is attached to the lower board. (See Illustrations). Soil is then dug or ploughed against the roots, firmed by foot and levelled off. Modern ploughs have an attachment so that after ploughing soil into the roots, that soil is firmed by rolling and a trench cut for the next row all in one operation. Whilst

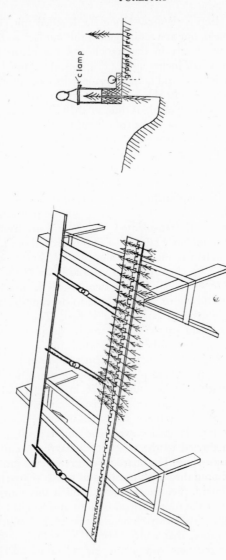

Diagram of an open transplanting board, set on trestles, being filled with seedlings in notches at correct spacing and to correct depth. The filled board is closed and clamped to hold the seedlings in position and set on the edge of the cut soil face

lining-out boards are being filled, a shelter covered with hessian is usually erected round the trestles where the people work filling the boards.

(c) **Spacing for Transplanting.** As transplanting means a considerable spreading out of the seedlings, it also means that this area has to be kept free of weeds. Therefore spacing should be as small as possible, consistent with giving the plants room to grow. For seedlings which are small but likely to stay only one year in the transplant lines, a spacing of one and a half inches between the plants and six inches between the rows should be used. For big seedlings likely to be two years in the lines, a spacing of two inches or more between plants, and ten inches between rows is recommended.

(d) **Lining-out in Beds and Bedding-out.** This has recently become popular because the beds can easily be hand-weeded or hoed without the worker going amongst the plants. A ten-foot transplanting board used for setting the seedlings in will give two beds each three feet six inches wide, and two alleys of one foot six inches. Care has to be taken in filling adjacent boards so that alley follows bed and so on.

(e) **Age and Size of Plants.** Apart from Spruces, most seedlings should be fit for lining-out at the end of one year. Spruces take two years. Apart again from Norway Spruce, which requires two years in the transplant lines, all others should be big enough for planting in the forest after one year in the transplant lines.

A one-year seedling is known as a 1 + 0 plant.
A two-year seedling is known as a 2 + 0 plant.
A one-year seedling, one year transplanted is a 1 + 1 plant.
A two-year seedling, one year transplanted is a 2 + 1 plant.
A two-year seedling, two years transplanted is a 2 + 2 plant.

The best size for planting is from nine inches to eighteen inches, but bigger in rank vegetation or smaller on bare exposed land. When fit for planting, the plants are loosened by fork or by machine, lifted, graded and tied in bundles of 25, 50, or 100, depending on size of plant, and heeled or "sheughed" in the ground ready for sending to the planting area.

Maintenance of Nursery Fertility. As intensive growing of tree crops would remove a considerable amount of food from the soil and the lifting of trees removes particles from the soil, and weeding also takes away soil from the nursery, care must be taken to ensure that soil balance and fertility are maintained. The humus content must always be kept high. Fertility is maintained by having a proper nursery rotation when humus may be added. Following the lifting of transplant lines that section is usually allowed to lie fallow during spring and early summer when it can be cultivated and weeds killed off. Following fallow, a green crop is sown about the month of June. This crop, which might be Lupins, Mustard, or Oats and tares, is dug or ploughed in when green before flowering or seeding takes place. Compost or leaf mould may be added at time of sowing green crop. After the green crop is ploughed in, the land is allowed to lie fallow until the next spring when seedbeds are prepared. Compost of hop waste, or hop waste and straw, or hop waste and bracken, if available, may be worked into the soil some weeks before the seedbeds are prepared. Seedbeds can be followed by transplant lines.

Heathland and Woodland Nurseries. As one of the major expenses of an agricultural type nursery is keeping it free from weeds, temporary nurseries in a small area of felled woodland, or on a poor bit of heathland, have been very successfully established. The top surface soil is not buried, but cultivated and the results have been the production of very good plants at little or no cost for weeding for some years. Compost must be added generously along with artificial manures as the heathland soils are not generally very fertile initially.

Propagation by Cutting. This is the method used for

the propagation of Poplars and Willows, as it ensures that that every tree propagated will have exactly the same properties as its parent. Cuttings of first-year growth about one foot long should be taken from the selected parent trees, care being taken that the parent is of canker resistant stock. These cuttings are trimmed below a bud and set about nine inches deep so that one bud is showing above ground. The stem should be cut on a slant just above this top bud. The soil should be free and sandy. Space the cuttings about one foot apart. In the spring the bud will develop into a shoot which may reach three feet or six feet in height and a root system will be formed. At the end of the growing season, cut back this shoot to about three inches above ground level, lift the roots and transplant at two feet apart, in rows about three feet apart. Next season the cut back plant will throw up a shoot which may grow from six feet to eight feet in that season. During the next winter these plants may be carefully lifted because of their big root system and planted on the planting site. Hedging plants, such as Lonicera nitida or Privet may be propagated by cuttings.

Propagation by Layering. Not often used for forest trees, but can be used for hedging plants or Osier Willows. A shoot is bent down to ground level, and an angle cut made on the under side. The shoot is then pegged down so that this cut is buried in the soil. When growth starts, a root system is formed at the cut, and a plant can be cut off the main stem when well rooted. Aerial layering is not practiced in Britain. A growing branch is cut below a bud on an angle and moist soil packed round the cut. The soil is enclosed in moss and then wrapped in a celophane bag. After a few weeks roots will develop at the cut and a rooted plant can be cut away from the main stem.

Propagation by Grafting. Only used in experimental work. If several twigs are taken off one good stock tree and are to be propagated, young plants of the same species must be available in the nursery. The top of the nursery stock is cut off on a slant as also is the end of a twig. The cambium layer of the twig is held against the cambium layer of the stock plant, the whole is bound round with twine and waxed over. In a short time the cambial layers will become united to produce a new plant which will be true to the parent tree.

Propagation by Root Suckers. A few tree species such as Lime and Poplars send out their roots fairly close to ground surface. From these roots young shoots are sent up above ground. If the roots of the parent tree are severed by spade close to these shoots, a new rooted plant is obtained. This may be planted direct in the forest or transplanted for a year in the nursery.

Propagation by Stool Shoots, or Coppicing. This is different from all other types of propagation as it is a propagation or regeneration of a tree or trees in a fixed site in the forest, such as Oak, Sweet Chestnut, etc. Certain species, if the bole of the tree is cut off above ground level, have the property whereby dormant buds on the butt of the stem will spring into life and shoots will develop. These stool shoots will develop into trees, and if again cut off will send up another generation of stool shoots.

CHAPTER IV

PREPARATION OF GROUND FOR PLANTING

The land available for planting is that which is left after
industry, building and agriculture have had their share.
But in many cases agriculture can benefit from forestry by
way of properly planned shelter belts. The plantable land
may be from, (a) Moorland and Downland, derelict and
uneconomic pasture. (b) Scrub covered areas. (c) Felled
Woodlands, probably with considerable regrowth on it.
(d) Sandy tracts by seashore, and (e) Poor moorland with
shallow or deep peat. This land may vary from small
scattered patches to large stretches of moorland. In all
cases various points must be considered in the preparation
of ground for planting.

(a) **Access Roads** throughout the area must be the first
consideration. All areas will require roads for getting into
the area for planting, protection from fire, maintenance of
the plantations and later for the removal of produce.
Whilst all the roads need not be made at this stage they
should at least be planned for three reasons, (1) to position
gates in fences and layout of drains, (2) it is easier to plan
road gradients before an area is planted, as the trees grow
up soon obscuring the topography, (3) it is a disadvantage
if roads have to be cut through solid plantations, with the
added risk of windblow.

(b) **Subdividing the Area.** The planting area is usually
divided into sections of land of manageable size called
Compartments. The planning of compartment boundaries
should be done on the ground and then surveyed and put
on a map of convenient scale, say six inches to one mile.
The area is compartmented for three main reasons, (1) For
fire protection and fire fighting, (2) For ease of extraction

of produce, (3) For management purposes. A compartment may include land which will require different species for planting, in which case the area to be occupied by the different species may be classed as sub-compartments, or stands.

On fairly flat or undulating ground the compartments can be more or less rectangular, based on the extraction roads. On sloping ground, triangular compartments often provide the shorter haul by horse or other means for the extraction of produce. If extraction roads run at about forty five degrees across a slope triangular compartments can easily be laid out. Fire breaks or fire rides between compartments should run up and down the slope, to make suitable places for stopping a fire, or starting a counter-fire. No definite size of compartments can be laid down, but anything between fifteen and thirty acres is a convenient size. A ride is a tract of land left unplanted between compartments, and main rides should be from thirty to thirty-five feet wide, and subsidiary rides twenty to twenty-five feet wide.

(c) **Enclosing the Land against Stock, Rabbits and Deer.** In nearly all areas it is essential to exclude rabbits and often stock (sheep and cattle), and in exceptional cases roe and red deer. Fencing is at present one of the biggest expenses in forming a plantation. The smaller and more irregular the area, the greater the expense per acre.

To exclude stock alone, a fence of five plain wires, with one barbed wire put on the top inside of the fence stakes or stobs may be necessary. If rabbit fence only, then two or three plain wires with galvanised wire netting on the outside is sufficient, if against rabbits and stock, then three plain wires, plus netting, plus one barb wire on the top inside of the fence will suffice. If a temporary rabbit fence is required one or two plain wires with netting is sufficient. These fence types are illustrated in the following figures. To exclude rabbits and deer, then a higher fence is required. This usually consists of five plain wires, the lower three

TEMPORARY RABBIT FENCE

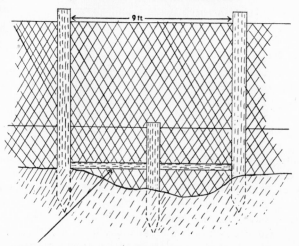

SPAR TO CARRY EXTENSION OF NETTING OVER
DEPRESSION

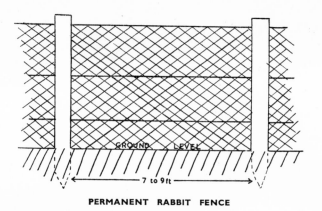

PERMANENT RABBIT FENCE

covered with rabbit netting wire, and the top two covered with wide mesh sheep netting, and above this one barb wire.

Materials used in Fencing.

Straining Posts, (Wood) 7 feet long with a top diameter at the smallest end of six to seven inches. Usually Oak or Larch. 9 feet 6 inches for deer fence.

Stobs or Stakes, (Wood). If round 3 inch top diameter, sawn, 3 inches square. Five feet six inches long and 8 feet for deer fence.

Turning Posts, (Wood). Round, 7 feet long with top diameter of 4 to 5 inches.

Stays or Struts, (Wood). Round 7 feet long with top diameter of 3 inches.

Plain Wire. This is galvanised and should be of No. 8 or 10 gauge. 1 cwt of No. 8 has a length of 540 yards.

Barb Wire. Two ply, 4 points six inches apart. 1 cwt equals 560 yards.

Tying Wire. No. 18 gauge galvanised wire. 1 cwt equals 6,200 yards.

Rabbit Netting. Usually 42 inches wide, No. 18 gauge, and 1¼ inch mesh. In 50 yard rolls. About 33 rolls per ton.

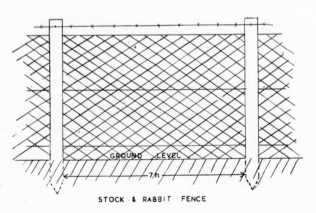

STOCK & RABBIT FENCE

Sheep Netting. Usually 24 or 36 inch wide, No. 14 gauge, with 4 inch mesh. In 50 yard rolls.

Staples. No. 8 gauge, 1½ inches long, 60 to 1 lb., 17 lbs. per 1,000.

Butterfly Ratchets, Galavanised. Not often used, but may be used for tightening the plain wires of a fence and remain in position.

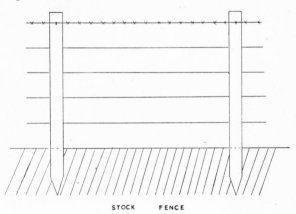

STOCK   FENCE

Layout of Fence. There are one or two points to be borne in mind in laying out the line of a fence.

1. If the boundary is a wall or a dry stone dyke, keep the fence line back about three feet on the inside of the wall.

2. The same applies to a mound or a bank of earth thrown up from boundary ditches. Such mounds are certain to be full of rabbits, and difficult to clear.

3. Avoid as far as possible putting a fence across the face of a steep slope, as this requires a higher fence to prevent vermin jumping the fence from above.

4. If possible avoid hollows where the fence may be covered with snow in winter.

5. Where the fence crosses a stream, find out the flood level, and keep the straining posts on the bank well back from the flood level.

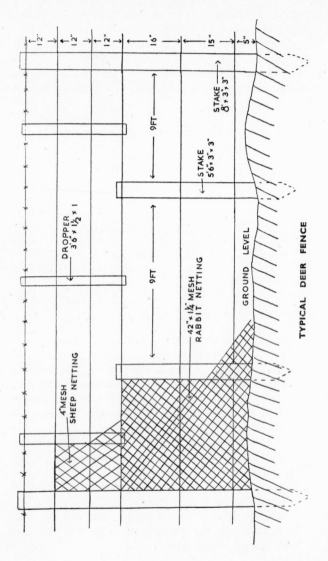

TYPICAL DEER FENCE

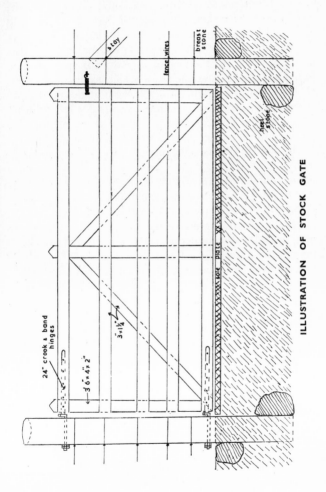

ILLUSTRATION OF STOCK GATE

stay

fence wires

breast stone

heel stone

sole plate

24" crook & band hinges

3'-6" x 4" x 2"

3" x 1½"

Erection of Fence. Having chosen and cleared the fence line, and it is proposed to erect a rabbit proof fence, the track where the bottom six inches of the wire netting will be buried (to prevent rabbits burrowing underneath), may be opened by plough. The position for the strainer posts should now be fixed from 150 to 200 yards apart starting from the gate posts at the roads which have already been planned. Dig the strainer holes at right angles to the run of the fence. Lower the strainers in so that 3 feet 6 inches are above the ground. Pack in a heel stone on the side opposite to the strain, pack in the soil and finish up with a breast stone at surface level on the side of the strain. Fix in stay.

Run out, strain and fix the bottom plain wire to the strainers. If the track for the rabbit netting was not opened by plough it should now be opened by spade. The fencing stakes should now be driven into the ground at the proper spacing and to such a depth that 3 feet 6 inches are above the ground. In crossing depressions short stakes may have to be added. Run out the plain wires, strain and fix to stakes by staples. Roll out the netting wire, slightly strain, and staple the top of the netting to the stakes. Tie the netting to the plain wire by three ties of tying wire between stakes, or by galvanised Nettlefold rings. The bottom six inches of the netting is then buried, at a slight angle sloping

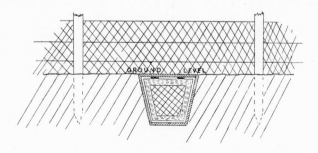

WATER BOX WITH HINGED LID IN DRAIN

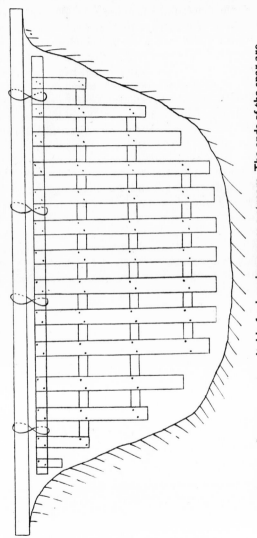

Diagram of a water gate suitable for hanging across a stream. The ends of the spar are fixed to strainer posts dug into the bank on both sides of the stream away from the fence, and where necessary the netting wire is fixed to other plain wires by ties. Make and hang the gates, ensuring that there is a sole plate in the ground where the gate hangs when closed, and that the gate is rabbit proof. Insert water boxes in drains and hang water gates where the fence crosses streams. A turning post is used where a slight change of direction is desired, or where sharp rises or falls occur in the fence line. To economise in the use of fencing stakes and at the same time maintain wire spacing and rigidity, the stakes can be spaced wider, with light wooden rods (droppers) of $1\frac{1}{2}$ inch square section positioned between the stakes.

(d) **Preparation of ground for Planting.** According to the type of land to be planted, there may be a variety of weedy herbaceous or scrubby vegetation growing on it, which has to be treated. If possible this preparatory work should be carried out in autumn or early winter. The following types of growth may require treatment.

Heather or Ling. If very rank may be burnt off, but burning compacts the surface of the soil, and before planting, the ground of the burnt area should be ploughed, or the soil should be aerated and broken up by mattock. Do not burn heather where near other young plantations, because of the risk of fire getting away.

Gorse (Whin). Cut to the ground and burn.

Broom. If dense, cut lanes through it at planting distances apart. Broom is liable to die off after a few years.

Bracken. Some people cut bracken in the young frond stage for two years before planting. This reduces the vigour of bracken, but adds expense.

Briar and Blackberry (Bramble). Should be cut and burned, but this is expensive. A motor scythe may be used, giving the driver hand protection against thorns.

Blackthorn. Should be cut over and burned.

Rhododendron. A big and expensive problem in places. Should be cut and burned if possible, and sucker shoots kept under control.

Scrub Birch and Hazel. Action depends upon density of crop on the ground. If fairly good stems, then it may be possible to sell standing to a small merchant dealing in this material, or give him the produce in return for clearing the ground. If fairly open, remove only trees which would interfere with the proposed crop. If dense and poor quality cut strips half a chain wide and burn before planting, leaving half chain strips uncleared; or cut groups in it. Groups about sixteen feet square, twenty feet apart centre to centre gives 109 groups per acre. Plant nine plants per group. If of mainly Birch with fairly tall crowns, the growth may be thinned out and underplanted with a shade bearing species, such as Beech, Hemlock Fir, Silver Fir, Norway Spruce, etc., depending on soil conditions and other site factors.

Regrowth on Felled Hardwood Areas. There are usually some good seedling plants and there may be good shoots from young stools. If there is a fair stocking on the ground of good valuable species, then cut back weed species and allow the good species room to grow. Any patches of pure weed species should be cut out and more useful species planted. If there is nothing worth retaining in the regrowth, then try to sell or give away the standing produce to a small merchant in return for getting the land cleared. If this is not possible, then cut strips or groups and burn, or completely clear the area. Tackle only a small patch each year as heavy weed growth will develop requiring cutting back for up to five years after planting. In all cases exclude vermin and deepen drains as the felling of the previous crop will have brought about a rise in the "Water Table" (see later) and will make the new crop more difficult to establish.

Old Coppice Areas. As produce from coppice is not so much in demand except in special localities, it may be better to let the coppice shoots grow on until they become of saleable size. In this case if the main roots from which the coppice shoots are springing are young roots, a moderate crop may result. If the quality of the coppice is low, then if possible sell it, or clear groups or strips and interplant with more valuable species. Hazel coppice, if once neglected, is not likely to grow on to saleable size. It should be clear cut and the area replanted with a quick growing conifer, e.g., Japanese Larch, to suppress the rapid re-growth.

In all work of preparation of ground for planting there is no need to be too neat and tidy, so long as the work done is sufficient to allow the planted trees to get away, with the least expense, as they will later suppress any weed growth. Try to avoid "girdling" or "ringing" trees to kill them off as the dead trees will always appear ugly. "Girdling" is cutting through the bark and cambium layer all round the tree, so that the tree eventually dies off.

(e) **Preparation of Soil for Planting.**

Fixing Sand Dune Areas. The best method of fixing sand which may blow is to thatch it with branchwood, especially conifer branches. Planting of Gorse, broom and marram grass have all been tried, but are not too successful. Trees can be planted easily through the branches.

Why We Drain. Soil is composed of a very large number of very fine particles in addition to the large pebbles and stones. These mineral particles may be of regular or irregular shape; between these particles in a well drained soil there should be air spaces, with a film of moisture round the soil particles. In a waterlogged soil there are no air spaces, the spaces between the soil particles being entirely filled with water.

In practically all soils, except completely water-logged soils, water will penetrate from the surface downwards to a certain depth. The depth at which a soil becomes saturated is known as the *Water Table*. The depth of water table varies all over the country, and plant roots are unable to penetrate below this level as there is no air in the soil. The benefits derived from drainage depend upon the depth to which this water table can be lowered, so that instead of a constant waterlogging, a movement of both water and air is established in the soil by drainage.

Trees vary considerably in their demands for water. Some will stand a wide range of moisture, although few will stand too much. The water in all cases must be fresh and not stagnant. On wet ground the failure of trees is due to:—

1. Lack of air in the soil. The roots, being unable to breathe, die off.

2. Boggy or marshy conditions means a low soil temperature.

3. Incomplete decomposition of humus, because conditions are unfavourable for bacterial activity, thus making the soil acid.

4. Red rot or heart rot is liable to occur through root decay. This is more likely to occur where thin gravelly soil overlies tenacious soil.

5. Windfall often happens where excessive water is present due to an impervious layer in the soil through which the water cannot penetrate. Windthrow occurs most often when gales follow heavy rain. If the soil is made permeable by drainage then there is a reduced risk of windthrow.

In an undrained soil the roots are confined to a shallow layer which in dry weather is sometimes deprived of the water available for the plant, so that the plant may even suffer from drought. In a drained soil, however, the roots are able to penetrate deeper, thus more water is available for the plant, and the plant will be in a better position to withstand a period of surface drought, except when recently planted.

In the drier regions drainage is carried out, not to lower the water table, but mainly to break up the surface soil and aerate it. Some of our glacial deposits of boulder clay are so compact and hard that they must be broken up to allow tree roots to penetrate. In many such soils at varying depths below the surface we find a layer of soil which is bound

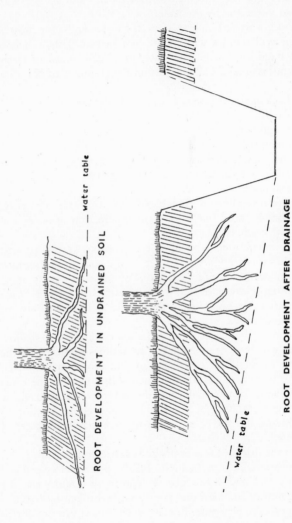

ROOT DEVELOPMENT IN UNDRAINED SOIL

water table

ROOT DEVELOPMENT AFTER DRAINAGE

water table

together in a very hard and compact band by an iron deposit. This is called a "pan" or "iron pan". In draining such ground it is essential to penetrate this pan and when this is done there is a freer movement of water, both upwards and downwards by capillary attraction, thus the soil is better aerated for tree root growth.

Drainage Work. In order to improve wet areas, the cause or source of wetness must first be found. If this is due to spring water it may be possible to catch the water where it rises and lead it off into a ditch before it can spread and render an area too wet for planting. The layout of the drains cannot be planned in an office, as each area with its different problems of topography, soil type, etc., must be considered on its own merits. If possible, drainage should be done about a year in advance of requirements to allow the drains to have effect before planting. Start draining at the lowest level and work upwards to a higher level, thus avoiding working in a building up of water. The whole drainage work, preferably including bottoming, should be completed before planting starts.

A drainage system of leader and feeder drains should be built up. The distance between drains will depend on the amount of water to be taken away, on the slope, and on the porosity of the soil. Feeder drains should not be too far apart; on areas where there is no peat, they should be spaced from one to two chains apart on fairly steep slopes, but closer where the slope is not so steep. The depth of drain will depend on the nature of the soil. On stiff soil the top width can be about three quarters of the depth.

Water will always flow in the direction of the steepest slope, and the best way to control this flow of water is to cut across the slope with as little fall as possible. Such drainage is called "contour" drainage as the drains follow very close to the contours. These contour drains are feeders running into a main drain or small stream. The feeders should enter the main drain at an angle of about 45°. The following types of drains are recognised:—

c

1. Leader or main drains.
2. Feeders or side drains, which may be contour drains.
3. Trap or catch drains which run along the top or bottom of a slope and cut off the flow of water, thus preventing an accumulation of water on the flats. Such drains can also follow the contours, but are usually bigger than contour drains across a slope.

Wet Soils with Deep Peat. Drainage on such soils is absolutely essential. The principle of drainage of these soils which are usually found on flat basins or on undulating ground in high rainfall areas, is the laying out of a system of parallel drains of such dimensions and spacing that the turfs from the drains provide a site for plants at the desired planting distances. These drains must all open into a main leader, in a herring-bone pattern, and if possible should be dug through the peat and into mineral soil for about three inches. In very deep peat this is not however possible.

These parallel drains are sometimes referred to as "turf" drains, because the surface turf is used for planting. If planting distance is 5 feet by 5 feet as with Norway Spruce, the drains will be spaced 27 feet apart, centre to centre. The drains are laid out at this spacing, and the sides cut 18 inches apart with a "rutter" spade. The turf is then cut across the drain with a cross-cut spade to give turfs of approximately 18 inches square. When cross-cutting the turfs a downward pressure is applied to the handle of the spade raising the turf out. These turfs are then dragged out, by a "pistol grip" handled drain drag, into five rows and turned upside down so that the vegetation of the turf is lying on the ground vegetation. This gives five rows of turfs at five feet spacing between the centres of the turfs, and three and a half feet between the centre of the outside turf and the centre of the drain. The drains may be spaced at 22 feet apart in high rainfall areas to give four rows of turf between drains.

Diagram of hand drainage on peat areas, showing spacing and size of drains and spacing of rows of turves between drains. Plants are then notched through the turves which had been laid at measured distances in the rows

Drainage on Felled Woodlands. On many woodlands felled during the war years the satisfactory growth of the former crop was only made possible by a system of artificial drains. Even where such a system was maintained in good order up to the time of felling, it is certain to have been damaged during the subsequent extraction of the timber. Old drainage systems should therefore be cleaned out thoroughly before replanting begins, provided that these old drains are properly sited. Particular attention should be paid to the downstream outlets which may have silted up.

(f) **Ploughing Forest Soils.**

In recent years, in order to reduce costs and improve larger areas of land with little increase in man power, there has been a great development of ploughs and of tractors to pull these ploughs on rough, soft and wet moorland.

The general power is by track-laying, or crawler tractors. The ploughs are strong and often have a subsoiling attachment.

Ploughing for Aeration. In many areas there is a very tight compact soil, generally resulting from glaciation. The rainfall is low and tree growth is usually poor. These areas are usually ploughed across the slope, following contours, thus preserving the moisture by a slower run-off. Spacing of furrows is generally that at which the forest trees will be planted, namely 5 feet, 5 feet 6 inches, or 6 feet. If there are old tree stumps or an iron pan below, the tine plough will break up the pan but turns out only a shallow furrow.

Ploughing for Drainage. In high rainfall areas where peat exists, it is very expensive to drain by hand, therefore, where possible, ploughs are used to cut drains and so provide turf on which the young trees may be planted. Ploughing in this case is usually done to provide a trap drain at the top of the slope, then up and down the slope to allow the water to run off; at the same time care must be taken that the run off is not too rapid to cause erosion.

Ploughing is not always done at tree planting distances, but may be at 10 feet, 15 or 20 feet, and the out-turned turfs cut by hand and spread at the required planting distances.

The advantages of ploughing are:—Cheapness, speed, extensive drainage or aeration of the soil, and suppression of surface vegetation, which reduces the cost of weeding plants after planting, allowing the trees to get away without competing with the vegetation. It may reduce the risk of fire, but it may hamper fire fighting and extraction of produce by the raised ridges produced.

Care must be taken to ensure that the out-turned turf has completely settled before planting. Strong heather growth often causes the out-turned furrow to be left springy, and if planted on before proper settling takes place, the roots of the young trees are liable to be left in an air pocket to dry out and die.

CHAPTER V

FACTORS TO BE CONSIDERED IN THE SELECTION OF TREE SPECIES FOR PLANTING

When travelling through the countryside one notes the changing colours due to the different foliage of the various tree species, but how often does one stop to think why there should be a change of tree species, and in other cases why there must be large stretches of the same trees. The change is obviously not made solely for the sake of amenity. There are many other factors which the forester must consider when selecting the tree species. Forestry is not like agriculture where most crops are annual. Whatever crop is planted is likely to be there for many years, and therefore to ensure that the correct species is chosen careful consideration must be given to many factors.

1. What species or mixture of species will the soil support and produce the greatest quantity of good timber.
2. How can the fertility of the soil be maintained and improved by the species or mixture of species.
3. What tree species will stand up to the climate, exposure, aspect and elevation of the planting site.
4. The possible future market for thinnings and final crop produce.
5. The possibility of fungal attack if an area of former broadleaved trees is to be replanted by a coniferous crop.
6. What species have done well on other areas near at hand, or under similar condition, and especially what species have failed in the locality.
7. The amenity of the district.

The Soil. Rocks are divided up into three main groups: *Igneous* or Primary rocks from which all other rocks have been derived; *Sedimentary* rocks which have been formed by the accumulation and consolidation of fragments and particles worn away from the Igneous rocks by various weathering agencies; and *Metamorphic* rocks which may come from both Igneous and Sedimentary rocks by alterations due to excessive heat or consolidation.

These rocks are broken down by various agencies such as, temperature variations (excessive heat and frost), rainfall, snow, plant and animal life, etc., to eventually become a soil as we know it, made up of particles of all sizes. There are few soils which have been produced from rock lying directly below. Most of the soils in Britain have been transported by the action of ice and water. Through the ages there have developed several soil types which may be recognised, but even these are subject to variation due to climate and topography, and due to the actions of man, animal and plant life. The main types are:—Brown Earth, Podzol, Peat, Rendzina, Gleys, Alluvial and transported soils such as sand dunes.

Brown Earths. These are developed mainly in south and south-east of Britain, where the climate is not excessively wet, but the summers warm. This is the type of soil to be found under natural oak forest. Some leaching of soluble salts may take place from the surface and thus there may be some acidity in the first few inches of the soil. There is no marked differentiation into layers as one digs down into a brown earth, and there is no great accumulation of raw undecomposed organic matter on the surface. To this group belongs our best forest soils.

Podzol. (Meaning Ash Grey). This soil type covers a considerable part of the British Isles, and develops where the rainfall exceeds evaporation, and where the summers are cool, and where there is free drainage. If we dig a pit into a Podzol, we find that there are several layers or *Horizons*. The surface layer typically consists of raw humus of partly decomposed plant remains woven into a caked appearance by the filaments of fungi. Beneath this is a

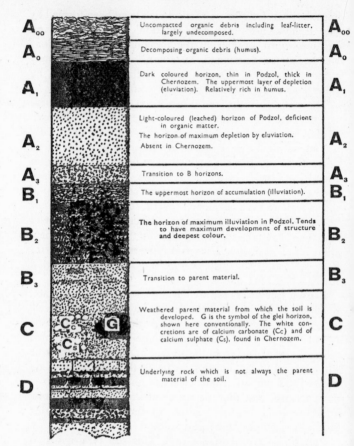

THE SOIL-PROFILE

humus layer which is decomposed and structureless. Below this humus layer is found a layer of varying depth which is partly bleached soil, which then passes into the leached or grey layer. This layer is leached of its iron and aluminium oxides by the downward movement of water.

Depending on the porosity of the soil this layer may extend down to about two feet from the surface. Then the B. Horizon is reached which is a layer of deposition, and there may be considerable cementing and compacting and often a definite blackish or reddish band of about one inch in thickness which is the pan layer. Below this there may be variation according to the locality or Geological formation forming the parent material.

Peats. These are produced where there is high rainfall and cool summers, such as the West coastal regions. It is not found on steeper hill slopes due to free natural drainage, but as soon as drainage is impeded, plant remains do not completely decay and the formation of peat starts. The texture and acidity of peat varies considerably according to the plants which grow on it. This type of peat is often referred to as blanket peat or blanket bog, and is formed by the occurrence of an impervious layer in the soil, and is distinct from the fertile fen peats.

Rendzina. These are immature soils found in chalk and limestone areas and developed into a soil with very good drainage, shallow, alkaline reaction. If allowed to develop naturally these would probably develop into brown earths with a crop of natural beech forest. These soils with alkaline reaction are often referred to as Calcareous soils.

Gleys. These are of fairly widespread occurrence, and may be closely linked with Podzols. The gleying is due to the presence of an impervious layer, impeding the movement of water. Gleys are found mainly on the clay deposits in the lower half and east of England.

Alluvial and other soils. Alluvial soils are generally fertile sands and silts over larger stones and boulders on raised river terraces, and not often available for forestry. Other soils may be infertile sand dunes, and soils formed following mining, especially after open cast mining has completely disturbed the structure of the underlying strata. These are of comparatively small area, but in cases it may be advisable to afforest such sites.

C*

The most important feature of soils as far as the forester is concerned is the mineral content and physical properties of the soil. These characteristics of the soil are usually reflected in the surface plant life, and now it is generally accepted that the surface vegetation can be often used to aid the choice of species for planting. Examples are given in the Appendices. The most important physical properties of the soil, are depth, tenacity and soil moisture, and the forester should be careful to study these properties before selecting his tree species. According to the size of the mineral particles, soils may be divided into silts, sands, sandy loams and clays, and usually, the higher proportion of clay the more fertile the soil. This is best illustrated by reference to the triangular soil texture diagram.

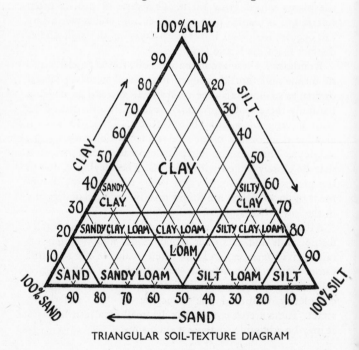

TRIANGULAR SOIL-TEXTURE DIAGRAM

Climatic Factors

These cannot be considered solely on their own, but must be linked up with topographical factors. The main features of the climate which affect tree growth, or which may prevent tree growth are:—Temperature including frosts, Rainfall, Wind and Sea Blast or Air Pollution.

Temperature. This does not limit the growth of trees within our longitude and latitude, but it may be a limiting factor in altitude. According to the mean summer temperatures we get variations from broadleaved to conifer plantations. The winter temperatures and especially the occurrence of frosts is much more important to the forester. According to topography, the early sun may strike on a slope which overnight had suffered from frost, and sudden heating would increase the effects of frost. The occurrence of late spring frosts should be noted as these will damage the young shoots, and the occurrence of early autumn or winter frosts may damage the winter buds before they have thoroughly hardened off for winter. The occurrence of frost hollows should be noted. These are hollows or valleys in which the cold air will collect on calm clear frosty nights, and damage would occur to young growth of species which are not so frost hardy. Temperatures will be affected by topography and aspect and elevation, and all factors must be considered together.

Rainfall. The lack of rain does not act as a factor which precludes the planting of trees in Britain, even on pure sands. It may limit the rate of growth in some of our more Eastern counties, and even on steep hillsides or ridges. But certain species will do better in high rainfall areas than in low rainfall areas, and vice versa. Therefore the forester requires to study the rainfall of his locality and its distribution throughout the year. The intensity of drainage adopted on the planting site and fall of the drains will also be influenced by the rainfall.

Wind, Sea Blast and Air Pollution. These can be combined for study. The intensity of wind and particularly gales may influence choice of species. Depending on elevation and topography, sea blast may affect trees several miles from the sea, and the risk of damage must be assessed, and a species more resistant to sea blast may have to be chosen. The direction and intensity of the wind will depend on topography, aspect and elevation of planting site, and the forester may have to consider the planting of a less economic species on the windward side to act as a windbreak or shelter belt. In or near industrial areas, air pollution by smoke and industrial fumes must be carefully considered before planting, as few tree species will really grow well where fumes are strong.

Elevation, Aspect and Exposure. These are all interrelated factors which must be considered together, as they, together with wind, are the foundations of local climate, and they are often the main reasons for the limitations of tree growth on certain sites. Elevation affects temperature, air becoming colder as one rises. Aspect affects temperature as on southern and western aspects the temperature is generally higher on average than on eastern and northern aspects. The average temperature is also generally higher in the west than in the east. Elevation and aspect affect exposure of a planting site; an area at sea level on the west coast may be more exposed than a hillside in the midland counties. Plant growth is usually later in starting on the east and north aspects and may therefore suffer less damage from late frosts than west and south aspects, where growth would have started earlier.

Markets. These are variable in their local demands for smaller sized produce, but generally the demand for larger sized timber is stable throughout the country. Any local industry may affect the choice of species, e.g., Ash for tool handles or sports goods may command a good price locally. Coppice crops of Oak or Sweet Chestnut may be useful in the hop districts. The demand for poles for the smelting industry may affect the choice of species. These are local and restricted markets. The forester will be planting on a long term policy for the production of large sized timber, although the demand for processed timber products will increase in this country in the future for paper pulp, hardboard, laminated wood, cellulose, plastics, etc. So that in effect the market for produce, whilst it may affect on a small scale, has no great affect on the choice of species when compared with climate, soil, etc. The aim should be to produce the largest quantity of best quality timber of the more valuable species such as Oak, Ash, Larch, etc., in the shortest economic period according to the local climate and soil conditions.

Tree Species of the locality. Although man has interfered with the bulk of our natural forests, one can gain much information from trees growing nearby, and from local records of the past. These may give an indication of species which have failed and the reasons for failure. A forester should therefore not restrict his thoughts to his own site, but should seek guidance from experience of tree growth on similar sites in his locality.

Replanting felled Broadleaved Woodlands. Certain fungi are always present in our woodlands and may, or may not, cause damage, according to variations in local conditions. One of these is known as Honey Fungus (*Armillaria mellea. Vahl.*) and is liable to cause damage by butt rot or even killing off young trees of conifer species if these are planted on a former hardwood or broadleaved site. Some conifers, such as Scots Pine, Corsican Pine, Sitka Spruce and Hemlock Fir are susceptible species, and should be avoided if possible for planting on such sites. European Larch, Japanese Larch, Hybrid Larch, Douglas Fir, and Norway Spruce are more resistant to the fungus and not so liable to be killed off. They may suffer some buttressing at the base often allied with butt rot.

Amenity. Each site must be considered individually from the following standpoints depending on what can be seen from roads and other vantage points: the layout of compartments with rides running across slope instead of up and down the hill will be the first factor to be considered, roadside planting with ornamental species such as Gean, Bird Cherry, Whitebeam etc., the breaking up of large dark green conifer blocks by odd pockets of Larches or broad-leaved species such as Ash or Birch may be possible. Anything that will give colour to conifer woods should be planted where possible even though they may not produce much timber. One important point to bear in mind is that favourite views can be obscured by trees when they grow up.

Pure or Mixed Woods. Mixed wood have several advantages over pure woods, such as:—

(a) Better timber of light demanding species, e.g. Ash, Oak and Larch can often be produced by mixture with shade bearing species. This is mainly due to the fact that later in life a mixed wood can be grown giving better natural pruning. This generally leads to a higher volume production per acre as the light passing through the crowns of the light demanders is used for growth of the shade bearers.

(b) The fertility of the soil is better preserved under a mixture. Pure crops of light demanders have to be opened out later in life, and allow the soil to deteriorate. Light demanders may be planted pure first and underplanted later in life with a shade bearing species. This is virtually a mixture. Where any broadleaved species might not grow if planted pure, it may grow in mixture and the humus from its leaves benefit the soil.

(c) Fuller utilisation of the soil generally results from the planting of a mixture especially if the tree species vary in their rooting systems, and utilise different layers of the soil.

(d) By mixing his woods the forester can produce timber to meet varying local demands and in certain areas this may be very important.

(e) Mixed woods are less exposed to damage by fire, wind, frost, insects and fungi because of their different demands and varying powers of resistance.

(f) Trees in mixture on difficult sites help one another to come out of check, and protect one another. For example, it is often advisable on chalk to plant some Scots Pine with Beech, as the Pine seems to help the Beech to get established. On heather sites if Sitka Spruce were planted pure, it would check for several years, but if planted in mixture with either Scots or Lodgepole Pine the two species nurse one another and grow more quickly.

(g) Often by planting a mixture, earlier returns are available. If Oak were planted pure it would be several years before there could be any return from sales of produce, whereas if Oak were planted in mixture with either Norway Spruce or Larch, we can get some early returns from the Spruce as Xmas trees and from the Larch as fencing or rustic work. Establishment costs may be reduced if a mixture is planted. Again if Oak were planted pure it takes a lot of plants per acre and these must be kept clear of weeds, but if planted in mixture with a quicker growing species, fewer plants of Oak are required and weeding costs will be reduced as the weeds would soon be smothered by the quicker growing species.

There is one problem with mixed woods, and that is in the management of them so that the mixture may be maintained. The rate of height growth, particularly in youth, is important. If we assume that growth conditions are favourable, the species may be grouped as follows, starting with the fastest growing group.

1. Douglas Fir, Japanese Larch, Sitka Spruce, Black Italian Poplar.
2. Hybrid Larch and Western Red Cedar.
3. European Larch, Hemlock Fir, Aspen, Ash, Lime, Elm, Beech, Sycamore, Maple.
4. Scots, Corsican, Austrian and Lodgepole Pines, Oak, Norway Spruce, and in early life Silver Fir.

The variations in the rate of growth of the species forming the mixture requires careful study. From this can be seen the fact that marking of thinnings in mixtures is more difficult. When forming a mixture it must be borne in mind that the climate and soil must be suitable for all species chosen for the mixture.

Various mixtures are planted such as, three plants of one species alternating with one plant of another species in the rows, or groups of sixteen or twenty five plants of each species alternating, or line mixtures of say, three lines of one species alternating with five lines of another species. If more than two species are used in the mixture, then various groupings may be used. It is inadvisable to have too intimate a mixture.

CHAPTER VI

SILVICULTURAL NOTES ON THE CONIFEROUS TREE SPECIES

Scots Pine. The leaves or needles are in pairs, stiff, often twisted and resinous, margins minutely toothed, two to three inches long. Winter buds are cylindrical at the base and taper conically at the apex. Cones almost truly conical in shape and from one to two inches long.

Native to Britain and widely distributed on the Continent. Although no races are distinguished it is advisable to use seed from good trees growing locally. Frost hardy and light demanding, resistant to wind, suffers a little from sea blast on coast, and liable to snow break at higher altitudes. Should not be planted pure over 800–900 feet, thereafter in mixture with Larch or Spruce. Will grow successfully over a variety of sites, but especially suitable for heather (ling) and bilberry sites and for light sandy soils in low rainfall areas. Used as a nurse for Beech on limestone and for Spruce on peat or heather. Not suitable for soft ground or areas liable to smoke or fumes. On bare, exposed sites, and on ploughed ground use 1 + 1 plant, but on areas of strong vegetation a 2 + 1 or even a 2 + 2 should be used. Rather slow growing. The most economic rotation is about 80 years. Can be regenerated naturally in Britain. If planted pure has to be kept open and this allows ground vegetation to develop and the soil to deteriorate; where conditions permit should be underplanted with a soil improver to maintain soil fertility. Liable to damage from Pine Weevil, Pine Shoot Beetle, Pine Looper Moth, etc., and in certain areas suffers extensive damage from Red Squirrel.

Corsican Pine. Needles are in pairs, about four to six

inches long. Fairly slender and flexible. Margins have small teeth and tips prickly. Winter buds are cylindrical, thin and tapering with concave sides to a long narrow point, and bud scales encrusted with resin. Cones are two to three inches long and about one and a half inches wide.

The tree is not native to Britain, being introduced in 1759. It has a fairly wide range from Spain to Greece, but it has its best development in Corsica. Has one or two races and the Calabrian form with stiffer needles and heavy branching should be avoided. Light demander but tolerates a little more shade than Scots Pine. Frost hardy and resistant to wind and sea blast. Should not be planted at high elevations and does best on light sandy soils at, or near, sea level, in low rainfall areas. More successful than Scots Pine on chalky soils. Avoid soft exposed sites. Suitable for smoky sites and for shelter belts as it retains its branches unless pruned. Sturdy 1 + 1 plants are best except where there is strong vegetation, when it may be necessary to use 2 + 1 plants. It is a comparatively fast grower and in a rotation will produce about 25 per cent more timber than Scots Pine. The best rotation is about 80 years.

Lodgepole Pine. Needles not flattened like Scots Pine, usually in pairs, margins minutely toothed and usually twisted, from two to three inches long. Winter buds usually encrusted with resin, cylindrical in shape, about half an inch long, with short domed points. Cones about one to two inches long, variable in shape, but often with a twist at the bottom.

Not native to Britain, discovered about 1805 in the mountains of Alaska, and is found in California. Introduced into Britain in 1853. Two races or varieties distinguished, the shore type with rough widespread branches, and the upright form growing tall and straight with narrow branching habit. Frost hardy, intolerant of shade, resistant to wind, the upright variety suffering little from snow damage, but the shore variety may suffer from snow damage if planted at higher elevations. Will grow on sandy coastal areas, or on poor deep peat if turf planted and given a dressing of basic slag, or on shallow peat on tough morainic knolls if turf planted and slagged. Shore variety is suitable for suppressing vegetation such as heather, and for this reason is often planted in mixture with Sitka Spruce. Used as a nurse on poor soils, but should not be planted on good soils. Planted as a 1 + 1 or a 2 + 1 plant, generally on turf, and slagged on poor sites. Suitable for shelter belts. Usually cleans itself of branches if upright form is planted at regular close spacing. Best rotation not yet fixed, but may in poor soils be used as a pioneer species on a short pitwood rotation.

Mountain Pine. Needles in pairs, stiffer than Scots Pine, usually remain longer (up to five years) on shoots. Winter buds cylindrical, more densely covered with resin than those of Scots Pine. Cone one to one and half inches long. Two or three varieties, including the creeping and erect forms. Frost hardy, stands exposure and snow. Used on exposed places for shelter as it retains its lower branches for a long time. Not grown as a forest tree except on very poor soils and then only as a nurse or for shelter. Plant as a 2 + 1 or a 1 + 1 if vegetation short. Used as a nurse for Sitka Spruce on poorer peaty sites where heather growth is fairly rank.

Austrian Pine. Needles in pairs, thick and rigid and from three to five inches long, not twisted. Margins serrated and points prickly. Cones two to three inches long, light brown and shiny.

Native of Austria, introduced into Britain in 1835. Not generally planted as a forest tree as its timber is not very good. Planted for shelter belts on exposed sites particularly on coastal areas as it is resistant to wind, and branches persist for long time right down to the ground. Could be used in place of Scots Pine as a nurse with Beech. The only types of soils to avoid for Austrian Pine are stiff and wet soils.

European Larch. Deciduous conifer having long and

short shoots. Needles appear singly on long shoots, but in tufts on short shoots, about one inch long, flexible, flattened, narrow and light green. Long shoots are from yellow to grey in colour, furrowed and non-hairy and having raised leaf cushions of previous years single needles. Cone about one inch long and three quarters of an inch in diameter.

Native of Central and Southern Europe, it was introduced into Britain in 1728. Several strains recognised, but those of North East and Central Scotland are most reliable. Frost tender when needles are young, but otherwise moderately hardy. Strong light demander. Resistant to wind and not liable to damage from snow. Exacting as to soil for planting. Moist well drained loam in open but unexposed site. Bracken with fine grasses and red stemmed moss may be used as a site indicator. Soil with natural drainage and certain northerly aspects are suitable. Avoid damp, ill drained, very dry, frosty sites, shallow soil over chalk, poor sands, peats, exposed sites near the sea, areas liable to smoke and fumes. Plant as a 1 + 1 or as a 2 + 1 plant. Liable to suffer from Larch Canker, Heart Rot, and "Die Back." Suitable for mixture with Oak or Pine. If planted pure should be underplanted later in life with such trees as Beech, Norway Spruce, Hemlock Fir or Grand Silver Fir. Produces very good quality lasting timber, but not our greatest volume producer.

Japanese Larch. Also deciduous conifer. Long shoots red to purple brown in colour. Leaf cushion long and nearly covering bud, whereas in European Larch this cushion stops short of the bud. Needles blue green, about one and a half inches long. Cones are globular with reflexed scales.

Native to Japan, first introduced into Britain in 1861. Moderately frost hardy, except when needles are young. Liable to windthrow on moist or fertile soils. Strong light demander, does not suffer much from snow damage. It will thrive on a wide variety of soils, such as poor shallow peats over compact soils where it is too hard and wet for

Pines, but where heather is the main vegetation. Grows quickly and will kill coppice shoots. On poor sites may be used as a pioneer crop on a short rotation. Will stand smoke and a fair amount of fumes from industrial areas. Avoid too dry areas and it is not worth planting on fertile soils, as timber too soft and liable to corkscrew habit. Does not suffer from diseases as European Larch does, but is liable to suffer butt rot on dry gravelly sites. Plant as a 1 + 1 or a 2 + 1 plant.

Hybrid Larch. Deciduous Conifer. Needles intermediate in colour to Japanese and European Larches. Shoots are more nearly the colour of European. Cones are also intermediate between European and Japanese.

Native to Scotland as first discovered at Dunkeld, Perthshire, early in the twentieth century. Grows faster than either of its parents, and straighter than Japanese Larch. Not liable to disease so far. Can be planted on soils much poorer than European Larch and almost similar to Japanese Larch, apart from the poorer sites. Fast grower, light demander, moderate frost resistant and fairly strong resistance against wind. Should be planted as a 1 + 1 or a 2 + 1 plant. Only plants from true strains can be recommended.

Douglas Fir. Needles singly on the shoots, flattened tapering at base where attached to shoot on a low elliptical peg-like cushion. Needles grooved on upper side with prominent mid-rib below, about one to one and a half inches long. Buds are resinous, chestnut brown and spindle shaped. Branchlets hairy. Cones pendulous three to four inches long with three-pronged bract scale protruding.

Native of North America and British Columbia it was introduced into Great Britain in 1828. There are three distinct varieties, the green, grey and blue. Douglas Fir is a very rapid grower on good sites, but the quality of timber when fast grown may not be very high. On very fertile soils may be inclined to twist. Douglas Fir likes a firm, well aerated soil of good depth, of a sandy rather than a clayey texture. Often does well on bouldery or rocky ground. It will grow on old gravelly river terraces at the foot of slopes where there is plenty of fresh moisture. It does best in the higher rainfall areas. Very liable to windblow on damp and soft soils. Unsuitable for exposed situations, heather ground, badly aerated or wet soils and areas subject to smoke and fumes. Can be planted as a 1 + 1 where there is no strong vegetation, but as a 2 + 1 where rank vegetation, and good planting is essential. Can be used for underplanting in scrub or coppice areas, or with European Larch, as it stands a considerable amount of shade. Suffers slight damage from Chermes or Adelges cooleyi scale insect, and a fungus Rhabdocline pseudotsuga. Rotation of about 80 years may be most economic.

Norway Spruce. Evergreen. Needles singly on shoot, stiff and often curved. Arranged all round the shoot, but usually twist to the upper side so that the underside appears bare. Quadrangular in section and pointing forward on the shoot. Leaves fall off after four to five years and leave a rectangular peg-like cushion. Buds conical with reddish brown scales. Young shoots reddish brown, non-hairy or with a few scattered hairs. Cones pendant, about four inches long and about one inch in diameter.

Native of Europe, especially of the mountain areas from the Urals to the Alps. There is no definite record as to when it was introduced into Britain, but has been cultivated for over four hundred years. It is best suited on moist grassy land where the common rush and tufted hair grass are abundant, and also on shallow peat. Does quite well on old hardwood sites as it is relatively immune from Honey Fungus. If on dry areas, old arable land and on clays it is liable to suffer from heart rot. It is moderately frost hardy and should be planted in preference to Sitka Spruce on low lying sites. It should not be planted on heather sites. Dislikes fumes and smoke. In real frost hollows and on heather areas it may be grown with Scots Pine as a nurse. It is not windfirm as it develops a very shallow root system.

It is a moderate shade bearer and the fallen needles tend to accumulate on the forest floor and render the soil slightly acid. It should be planted as a 2 + 2 plant.

Sitka Spruce. Needles singly on shoot, flat, long sharp points, about one inch long, and are arranged all round the branchlets. They are green above and grey below because of the stomatal bands, and the combination gives a blue-green appearance. Buds are small and egg shaped. Cones are cylindrical with rounded tops, from two to four inches long, light brown in colour with scales which are papery to touch.

Previously known as Menzies Spruce from Menzies who discovered it in 1792. Sitka is native to a small coastal region of western Canada and Vancouver. It was introduced into Britain in 1831. It will grow on a wide variety of soils, and situations from sea level in South England to altitudes over 1,500 feet in the North and West of Scotland. It has proved to be a useful tree at high elevations, and the introduction of this tree has made possible the afforestation of large tracts of more difficult and infertile land in Britain. It stands exposure very well, but not very windfirm in moist sites. Stands smoke and fumes fairly well. Thrives on most kinds of peat and succeeds better than Norway Spruce on the poorer types of Moorland. Avoid frosty or very dry sites. Best planted in mixture with a Pine (Scots or Lodgepole) on heather sites. Unsuitable for use in former coppice or scrub areas as it is liable to attack from Honey Fungus. Best planted as a 2 + 1 or even a 2 + 2 on sites with very rank vegetation, but too old plants are apt to be too big for exposed sites. Shallow planting or planting on turf is advisable. On poorer sites treat with manures such as basic slag or ground mineral phosphate.

Omorika or Servian Spruce. Needles singly on shoots, flattened on top and rounded below. Needles on upper surface overlap and point forward. Needles come to a small sharp point. Cones are glossy brown, usually with considerable resin, egg shaped, about two inches long, and tapered to a point. Branches short, resulting in spire-like tree. This Spruce has a restricted natural distribution in Yugoslavia, where it grows on soil overlying limestone rock. It was introduced into Britain in 1889. It may be grown under similar conditions as Norway Spruce, but is more frost hardy, and will even grow on poorer and more exposed sites. If seed were available this species would be used more extensively than at present. It flushes late, thereby escaping injury from spring frosts. Rate of growth is slower than Norway Spruce. Suitable for planting on shallow peat over glacial drift. Plant as a 2 + 2 plant.

Common Silver Fir. Young shoots have sparse short fine hairs. Needles arranged in two rows on the upper surface of the shoot, and are shining green. Winter buds small with few bud scales. Cones erect, falling to pieces when ripe leaving a bare axis. Cones are four to six inches long and two to three inches in diameter.

This species is widely distributed in central and southern Europe. It tends to grow mostly in the mountain regions. It was introduced into Britain over three hundred years ago. When shoots are young they are liable to damage from frost, but otherwise moderately hardy. It thrives best in a deep moist loam, but will grow on clay or sandy soil. It is windfirm and can be used for shelter. In fact it can be used on very bare exposed sites. It will stand some shade and can be used for underplanting of Oak or Larch. Most suitable plant for planting is a 2 + 2.

Grand Silver Fir. Needles are on a flat plane in two rows. Those on the upper row are shorter than those on the lower row, which may be about an inch long. Young shoots pale green and glossy. Winter buds small, blunt and resinous. Cones erect, about four inches long and one to one and half inches in diameter; no bract scale visible.

Native to North America it was introduced into Britain in 1832. It grows best in a deep well drained moist loamy soil. Avoid frost hollows and poor soils, particularly those inclined to be acid. Does better in the wetter west. It will bear slight shade but is not much used for underplanting. Fairly frost tender and liable to suffer from windblow on undrained soils. Large volume producer and can be grown fairly dense, but not on areas where liable to heavy snowfall as it will suffer badly. Best planted as a 2 + 2 plant.

Noble Silver Fir. Needles about an inch long with a groove on the upper surface, bluey-green in colour, with rounded tips. They are crowded on the shoot and lie flat along the shoot at their base, then turn upwards. Cones erect, cylindrical, up to eight inches long and two to three inches in diameter, disintegrating when ripe leaving a central axis, and the bract scales protrude from the cones.

Native of North America, it was first introduced into Britain in 1825. It does best on well drained loamy soils, but will tolerate more acid conditions than other Silver Firs. It does well up to fairly high elevations, but very poor soils and exposed places should be avoided. Plant as a 2 + 1 or a 2 + 2. May suffer from damage by a very minute insect of the *Chermes* family in warmer localities.

Hemlock Fir (Western Hemlock). Needles arranged in two ranks, uniform in width up to their rounded tips, with minute spines on margins. The needles are grooved on the upper side, and are from one half to an inch long. Young shoots are slender and drooping at the tips, greyish in colour and hairy. Buds are small in leaf axils. Cones are borne singly and have no stalk, about one inch long and half an inch in diameter.

Hemlock Fir is native of Alaska to British Columbia, and was first introduced into Britain in 1851. It grows rapidly on moderately fertile soil, but can be used on poorer exposed moorland sites. Excellent for underplanting or planting in old coppice areas, and for beating up other conifers as it is a fairly strong shade bearer. It thrives best where there is a little shelter. It is unsuitable for dry sandy soils. It will start away quicker on upland heaths if planted in mixture with a species of Pine. It is windfirm, fairly frost hardy, and is more suited to the Western half of

Britain where there is a higher rainfall. Should be planted as a 2 + 1 or 2 + 2 plant.

Red Cedar (Thuya). The branches are horizontal and often drooping at the tips. The leaves on the shoots are scale like, pointed, and each has an inconspicuous resin gland on the back. They are dark green above and usually have white areas below. When bruised the leaves are aromatic. Cones are about half an inch long, erect and green when young. When mature at the end of one season they are brown and the scales are reflexed. The bark is light red or brown and divided into ridges by shallow fissures, and between these the scaly bark peels off.

Native of Western Canada and North America, it was introduced into Britain in 1853. It is fairly accommodating as to soil, but will do best on good loamy soil and heavy clays. Poor soils, sour peats and frosty sites should be avoided. Thrives best in sheltered situations, but will grow at fairly high elevations, moderately exposed sites and near the sea. Will stand shade and is therefore very useful for underplanting, and can be used on poorer land which had previously carried coppice or Oak. Very wind firm and therefore suitable for shelter belts or hedges. A fungus, *Keithia thujina*, which damages and kills the leaves and shoots has prevented extensive planting. Best planted as a 2 + 1 or a 2 + 2 plant.

Lawson's Cypress. Leaves are scale-like in pairs and on vigorous trees may be pointed. The branchlets are flattened. The lateral leaves are keel-shaped, but those on the upper and lower surfaces are flattened. Cones are about one third to one half inch in diameter, have a short stalk, and are reddish brown and the scales do not overlap, but are compressed at the edges.

Native of Oregon and California, it was introduced into Britain in 1854. Mainly planted for ornamental purposes, for hedges or for shelter. It requires a good deep soil preferably in a site which is not too exposed. It stands shade well and is useful for underplanting of open Oak or Birch.

Should not be planted on dry sites, or on heather areas. Liable to fork, and to suffer damage from snow, and is not windfirm. Not grown extensively, but if planted should be as a 2 + 1 or a 2 + 2 plant.

Monterey Cypress. The lateral leaves, which are scale like, cannot be distinguished from the other two rows and the branchlet has a four sided appearance. The leaf tips are swollen but have no white patches. Cones are up to one inch in diameter, globular, and are made up from a few hard shield shaped scales, and are shining brown when mature.

Native of a small coastal area of Monterey, but has been planted extensively in Australia, New Zealand etc. It was introduced into Britain about 1838. Planted as an ornamental tree and for hedges, and is useful as a tree for shelter belts on the south coast. Will grow moderately well in warm moist localities up the West Coast. Subject to windthrow on soft ground. It will endure a little shade. Plant as a 2 + 1 plant, but not recommended for large scale planting as it is rather difficult to establish.

Nootka Cypress. Branchlets flattened like Lawson's Cypress. Leaves dull green and have an unpleasant smell when rubbed. They are in opposite pairs and sharp pointed. Male flowers are yellow, whereas in Lawson's they are crimson. Cones ripen in second year and are about the same size as Lawson's.

Native of Western North America, it was introduced into Britain about 1853. Planted in Britain mainly for ornamental purposes. Sites similar to Lawsons will suit this species. Fairly windfirm and hardy.

CHAPTER VII

SILVICULTURAL NOTES ON THE BROADLEAVED TREE SPECIES

Pedunculate Oak. The twigs are silvery to grey, fairly stout with winter buds blunt and oval in shape clustered at the tip of the shoot. The twigs are not hairy, but have scattered and raised lenticels on their surface. Leaves are not hairy, and at the leaf base are two lobes. The acorns are on stalks about two inches long.

Native to Britain, the Pedunculate Oak is usually found on heavy and damp clays of lower altitudes. This Oak should be planted on sites where the vegetation is of birch, hazel, Aspen, bramble, dog rose, bluebell, honeysuckle, ivy and dog's mercury. It should not be planted where the vegetation is of a heathland type. It should only be planted on the best sites, although it will grow on moderate soils. As it is a light demanding species it will not tolerate much overhead cover, and if planted amongst scrub trees these will have to be carefully watched so that they do not interfere with the development of the Oak. Susceptible to damage by late spring frosts. Whilst it may be grown from acorns sown in little patches on the planting site, it is more successful to plant one or two year old seedlings. The spacing should not be too wide. Planting must be very carefully done by spade to ensure that the deep tap root is well set in. It is best to screef off the surface vegetation for about one foot square before planting the tree, as this will enable the plant to grow without weed competition for some time and it will be more readily seen when weeding. To plant Oak pure means that the whole area has to be weeded every year for five to eight years, and it will be many years before there are any returns as Oak grows so slowly. If planted in row mixture with a quicker growing nurse species such as Larch, Norway Spruce or even Scots Pine at times, there will be some returns earlier from these conifer species, and the ground occupied by them will not generally require weeding for more than three years. About three rows of conifers alternating with five rows of Oak is a good mixture. But care must be taken that the conifers are removed before they are allowed to interfere with the development of the Oak.

Sessile Oak. Botanically it differs from the Pedunculate Oak by the fact that the leaf base is wedge shaped, the leaves have short stalks, the veins go to the tips of the lobes only, and there are hairs on the under surface of the leaves. The acorns are more or less without stalks.

Native to Britain, the Sessile Oak is usually found naturally on lighter soils such as those derived from sandstone, and is found at higher elevations than the Pedunculate Oak. Gives good results on deep, porous and well drained soils. Vegetation of Fern, wood anemone, wood sorrel usually indicates sites suitable for Sessile Oak. Less frost tender than the Pedunculate. Very wind resistant. Stands more shade than the Pedunculate Oak. Usually planted on soils which are not suitable for pedunculate, and in mixture with conifers to act as a soil improver. Careful planting of one or two year old seedlings is the best method of establishment. Suitable for coppice if it is desired to grow a coppice crop. Requires weeding for several years, but on usual planting sites the weed growth is not so strong as on the Pedunculate sites.

Red Oak. Has a leaf of six to eight inches in length which turns to a dull red in autumn. On the underside of the leaf there are hairs in the axils of the leaf veins. The acorn cup is shallow.

Native of America and Canada it was introduced into Britain in the eighteenth century. Not usually planted on any large scale, although it is a much quicker grower in early life. It is much less exacting than the other Oaks, but does not do well on limey soils. It can be planted on poor acid soils. More frost hardy and will stand more shade than the other species. May be grown on a short rotation as a pioneer species. The timber does not compare with that of the other Oaks in strength or durability, but is useful for less exacting purposes. Planted as a one or two year old seedling, either pure or in row mixture with conifers.

Beech. The young shoots are smooth and have a zigzag appearance. The buds, which are chestnut brown in colour, are spindle shaped and stand out sharply from the shoots. The buds are arranged alternately in two rows on the shoots. The leaves are oval in shape with serrated edges, indentated, and when young these edges are covered with fine hairs which disappear as the leaves get older. Two three-sided fruits are produced in a hairy cup.

Native to the South of England, Beech is usually found on fertile loams, well drained, overlying chalk and lime-stone soils. Unsuitable for heavy, cold and waterlogged soils. Frost tender and liable to suffer damage from spring frosts. Liable to suffer from drought on shallow soils. Strong shade bearer and therefore suitable for under-planting where there is a plentiful supply of soil moisture. If a mixture is proposed it must be borne in mind that Beech grows very quickly in youth, and may out-grow the other species of the mixture. Beech is very difficult to establish where there is no overhead shade, but can be planted with nurse species. Scots or Corsican Pines are suitable as nurses as they will grow quicker than the Beech and so give shelter to the Beech, and row mixtures either of one or two rows of each species alternating are most suitable mixtures. Suitable for shelter belts and may be used for fire belts as it will kill out all ground vegetation. A useful soil improving species.

Sycamore. Young shoots coarse, light brown, lenticels reddish. Leaf large and five lobed, margins serrated, leaf stalk red. Buds have green scales with dark brown margins, and stand out at a wide angle to the stem, opposite to each other on the stem. Fruit joined in pairs with long seed wings.

Not native to Britain, but introduced about the thirteenth century from Europe. A tree which will grow on moderate to good soils, and unsuitable for poor moorland except as a shelter belt tree. Suitable for planting on coastal areas, and possibly in smoky areas. Suffers from late spring frosts, but more frost hardy than Ash. A strong shade bearer when young it requires full light in later life. Should not be planted pure over large areas, but in mixture with other species on good moist fertile sites. Suffers bady from damage by grey squirrel. Best planted as a 1 + 1 or 2 + 1.

Ash. Buds opposite on the stem, black from minute hairs. Twigs grey-green and show large leaf scars. Leaves compound with up to twelve stalkless leaflets and one end leaflet. Fruit in clusters, with a seed enclosed in scale which is prolonged into a wing about one inch long.

Native to Britain, and very widely spread, mostly on non-acid soils. Very exacting as to soil, if it is to grow rapidly and produce good quality timber. Frost tender, but stands a good bit of exposure. It will tolerate shade when young, but is a light demander from early life onwards. Plant Ash only on a small scale on the very best sites where there is plenty of free moving fresh moisture, such as on the slopes of river banks on lime rich soils. Plants which indicate sites suitable for Ash are Dog's mercury, garlic, nettle and meadow sweet. Best planted in mixture with a frost hardy species, or in the shelter of short scrub or coppice, using good big plants. Will often suffer from Ash bud moth, and frost killing leading bud, causing the tree to fork.

Birches. Buds are spirally arranged on the twigs, small and reddish brown. The twigs are slender warty in pendula variety, and hairy in pubescens variety. The bark in the pendula variety is smooth, white and papery above, but usually rough and furrowed below. Seed produced in catkins.

Native of Britain, it is found over a wide variety of soils and up to high elevations. Very hardy and light demanding. Does not produce a high volume of timber, but timber is usually of good quality and useful for turnery work. Not usually planted pure but useful as a nurse for Spruce on frosty sites. However it requires to be watched in case it whips the conifer trees. Can be grown to useful size on many sites. Rotation should be about 60–80 years. Plant as 1 + 1 or a 2 + 1 plant.

Spanish Chestnut. Twigs are brown, stout and ridged. Leaf scars prominent. Lenticels appear as white dots. Buds are alternate on lateral shoots, but may be spirally arranged on erect shoots. The buds are rounded like those of Oak, but only two bud scales are visible. Leaves are from seven to nine inches long tapering to a point, and have strongly serrated edges. Fruits are formed in the shape of a hairy or spiny cupule, and enclose four nuts.

Imported into Britain many centuries ago, but has not spread far north. It does well on well drained loams and sandy loams. Should not be planted on heavy clays, or poor sandy soils. Can be planted for coppice on soils overlying limestone, but is highly unsatisfactory on very lime rich soils. Very frost tender and suffers especially from spring frosts. Moderate shade bearer in youth but strong light demander after twentieth year. Should be planted only where the climate is mild. Where produce can be sold it should be grown as a coppice crop on a rotation of about twelve years, or even up to sixteen years. If planted to grow as timber, it should not be planted as a mixture, but only on a restricted scale, where it has been known to grow well in the past.

Poplars. Buds are arranged spirally on the shoots, long, narrow and generally sticky. There are many hybrids. In the Black Italian Poplar the leaves are large, coarse with curved serrations, ovate with sharp pointed apex, and base nearly straight. One of the fastest growing trees in Britain. Grows best on loamy soil in sheltered situations, where the water table is not far below the surface, not waterlogged or near stagnant water. Can be planted on clays, but growth much slower. Not suitable for acid peats. Not suitable for planting on old woodland site where there is dense re-growth. May not grow so well in North England, Wales and Scotland. Small patches or rows on river banks are suitable for Poplar. Of the numerous varieties the following are recommended as being less liable to canker and disease:— *Populus serotina*, *Populus gelrica*, *Populus robusta*, and *Populus berolinensis*. The following species should be avoided:— *Populus trichocarpa*, *Populus regenerata*, *Populus marilandica* and *Populus generosa*. Start with a cutting, for two years in the nursery and then plant out. Plant at from 18 to 24 feet apart on mounds. Keep very well weeded so that there is no competition for the moisture available. Prune trees likely to go on to final crop.

Aspen. Winter buds small and pointed, sticky and glistening brown but not odorous. Leaves almost round about two inches in diameter, not hairy (except on sucker shoots), leaf stalk flattened at right angles to leaf. Leaves spirally arranged on shoots. Not planted much except for the match making industry. Fairly frost hardy, but requires moderately good loamy or silty soil. Avoid dry, sandy, or waterlogged areas. Strong light demander. Can be used as a nurse on suitable sites for a more valuable species. Plant as a 1 + 1 and keep open during growth.

Alder. Leaves spirally arranged, almost round or pear-shaped in outline, doubly serrated margins, dark green above. Leaf stalk about half an inch long. Buds stalked, spirally arranged, with greyish white bloom on bud scales. Shoots are violet brown in colour.

Native to Britain, and found on wet sites. Will grow on very infertile soils where wet, and on swampy sites liable to flooding, but not on peats to give timber. Light demanding. Can be used as a nurse or pioneer species on wet sites with other more valuable species (e.g. Sitka Spruce), in groups of

D

each species. Plant as a 1 + 1 plant. May be grown as coppice and the timber used for turnery.

Lime. Twigs smooth, reddish, zigzagged in outline. Buds alternate, stout, reddish brown and glistening. Large leaves, heart shaped, not hairy, with fine serrated edges. Not planted as a forest tree on any large scale. Will grow on fairly dry fertile soils. Slight shade bearing, and could be used for underplanting Oak when it is opened out in later life. Gives very good coppice growth, and suitable for shelter belts, fire breaks and amenity planting. Useful for beekeepers as bees get much honey from flowers.

Elms, Maple and Horse Chestnut. Planted on a very restricted scale. Confined to fertile sites and for amenity. Elm can be used as a nurse as it is frost hardy, but suffers from Dutch Elm disease. Elm should not be planted near roads or buildings, as when it gets older it is liable to windblow and windbreak without warning. Maple characteristics and requirements are similar to those of Sycamore. Not planted on any large scale. Horse Chestnut is planted solely for amenity. Uses for their timbers are restricted and therefore not planted on any great scale, as more valuable species can be planted on similar sites.

CHAPTER VIII

PLANTING

As many of the woods in Britain have been felled fairly recently, there is, at present, little opportunity for Natural Regeneration. By natural regeneration is meant the opening out of old woods to allow the seeds to fall on the ground and germinate naturally, thus giving a new crop without the necessity of planting. Planting has several advantages over natural regeneration, such as:–

1. Planting is more independent of seed years, and therefore time is saved in establishing a crop, as good seed years often occur at intervals.

2. Soil cover is established more quickly.

3. If an even aged wood is planned then this is best achieved by planting.

4. If failures occur it is easier to replace by planting than to wait for natural regeneration.

5. New species can be introduced, whereas in natural regeneration only the existing species on the ground may be reproduced.

6. Planting is often cheaper than natural regeneration, especially if many blanks occur in the regeneration, and have to be filled artificially by planting.

Season for Planting. Planting may be carried out any time after the growth of autumn is finished, from about the end of October to March or even into April if the weather is not too dry. In exceptional cases, for example on high ground where it has not been possible to plant because of snow lying, planting of such species as the Spruces may go on into the first week of May, but much depends on the dryness of the weather and the stage of growth of the plants.

Trees which come into leaf early, or trees which start growth early should be planted first. In warmer localities deciduous trees before conifers. Conifers should, if possible, be planted before their buds start to grow, and the sequence may be :— Larches, Pines, Douglas Fir, then Spruces. Warmer exposures should be planted before colder ones as growth starts earlier on the warmer sites. Planting of wet or exposed sites should, if possible, be left until spring.

Planting Tools. In order to get good results from planting, one essential is to use the proper tools according to the planting ground. On hard or stony ground the best tool is the planting mattock. For soft ground the dibble may still be used in places, but it is not now so popular as with poor workmanship the tree roots may be badly bunched. It could be used on sand areas and on turf planting, and in planting the out-turned furrows of ploughing. The semi-circular spade is not now so popular, but it was used in turf planting to take out a plug of soil, the plant inserted in the hole and the broken up plug of soil replaced. There are several varieties of spade suitable for planting such as a partly worn garden spade, "Schlich," "Norfolk" and Mansfield" spades. (See Illustration).

Planting Methods. In Arboriculture it may be possible and desirable when planting to plant the tree with a ball of soil enclosing the roots. This is called "Ball" planting. In Silviculture this is not possible because of cost and the "free root" system is the one adopted.

1. Mattock Planting. Where the vegetation is rank, it may be necessary to screef off the surface vegetation for about a foot square using the blade of the mattock. The mattock end is then driven into the ground and the handle lifted so the mattock breaks up the soil. The blade is then driven in and the handle pulled and lifted towards the planter so that a slit is made. The tree roots are then hung down into this slit, the soil allowed to fall back on the roots, and the soil is firmed by the heel of the planter's boot.

2. Dibble Planting. The dibble is pushed into the soil or turf to make a hole for the plant. The plant roots are inserted into this hole and spread as much as possible. The dibble is then inserted at an angle beside the plant, pulled

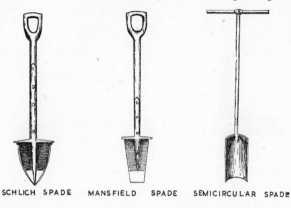

SCHLICH SPADE   MANSFIELD SPADE   SEMICIRCULAR SPADE

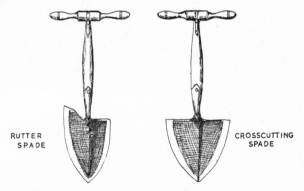

RUTTER
SPADE

CROSSCUTTING
SPADE

up so that the soil is pressed against the roots of the plant. The dibble has gone out of favour mainly because the plant roots are bunched up and not spread out. Used on free ground only.

3. Semi-circular Spade. Used only on turf planting. That is where a turf has been turned out of the soil and turned over so that the vegetation of the turf is lying on the ground vegetation. The spade is driven into the turf, turned and pulled out so removing a plug from the turf.

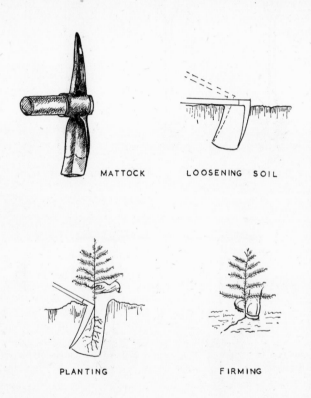

MATTOCK   LOOSENING SOIL

PLANTING   FIRMING

The plant roots are then spread out in the hole thus made and the plug which had been removed is broken up and filled into the hole, and the plant is then firmed by the heel of the planter's boot.

4. Pit Planting. Used mainly in Arboriculture. A hole about nine inches square, or more for bigger rooted plants, is dug about nine inches deep, making sure that the surface soil is set to one side, and poorer soil to another side of the hole. The plant roots are then spread out into the hole or pit, the best soil spread over them and then the poorer soil on top and then the surface turf, if any, is replaced and firmed.

5. Mound Planting. Very seldom used, except with Poplar planting. A mound of soil is built up to about a foot high. The roots of the trees are then planted into the top of this mound using an ordinary garden spade. This method is used to keep the plants free from the surrounding vegetation and soil moisture.

6. Notch Planting. This is the most common method used in tree planting. It is used where the soil is free, or soft. If done carelessly, the notch *may* open in dry weather, the tree roots dry out and the tree die. The notches must be vertical and deep enough to allow the tree roots to hang full length and not bend over.

Using the "Mansfield" or "Schlich" spade a vertical notch is made by driving the spade into the ground. The plant is inserted in the notch and the spade is then driven into the ground alongside the first notch and pulled over to close the notch and press the soil round the tree roots.

Using the "Norfolk" or garden spade, two or three notches are made in the ground in the shape of an inverted T, or an L or an H. With the inverted T or L notch the spade is driven into the ground with the edge of the spade towards the planter. With the back of the spade towards the planter a second notch is made, cutting across the first notch. The spade handle is then pressed down so that the notch opens and allows the plant to be inserted. The plant is held by the tip so that the roots hang freely in the notch. The spade is then removed and the soil pressed back against the tree by the heel of the planter's boot, without skinning the tree.

7. Turf Planting. The upturned turfs have been spread out in advance when draining. By planting time the turf will have settled and the two layers of vegetation in contact

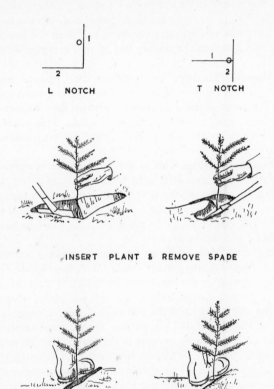

L NOTCH   T NOTCH

INSERT PLANT & REMOVE SPADE

HEEL IN FIRMLY

with one another should be beginning to rot. The turf is slit vertically from one side to the centre by spade. One side of the turf is raised, the roots spread out, the turf replaced and pressed against the roots. The tree now stands in the centre of the turf with its roots where two layers of vegetation are rotting, thus giving aeration and nutrients and keeping the roots from a soil which may be still wet and cold. The notch is often made on the side of the prevailing wind so that the plant will be blown against a solid part of the turf, and so, not liable to blow over. Care must also be taken in some kinds of peat that the notch is not likely to open when the drying spring winds come: this causes losses due to the plant roots drying out. Plants *may* be dibbled into the turf.

8. Planting on Ploughed Ground. As mentioned earlier under the preparation of the soil for planting, the outturned furrow may be of peat in the wet areas, and of soil where the ploughing has been carried out for aeration. The best place for planting the tree in the soil will depend on whether it is on a dry or wet site. On a dry site the plant may be planted in

D*

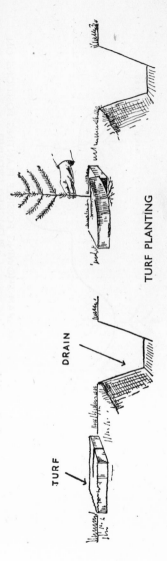

TURF PLANTING

DRAIN

TURF

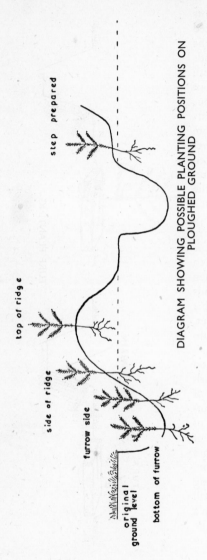

DIAGRAM SHOWING POSSIBLE PLANTING POSITIONS ON PLOUGHED GROUND

the bottom of the furrow where it is likely to get most moisture, or on the furrow side. In wetter areas, where the ploughing has been done for drainage, the young trees may be planted on the side of the ridge, or on the top of the ridge as illustrated. If the soil is fairly free, dibble, "Schlich," garden spade or mattock may be used to make the notch for the young trees. In peat, a garden spade or "Schlich" spade is probably the best. If the out-turned spoil is very deep, it may be necessary to cut out a step in the spoil before planting, to ensure that the tree roots reach through to where the two layers of vegetation meet.

Density of Planting

The guiding principles for spacing in planting are:—

1. Cost of Planting. Wider spacing means fewer trees to

be planted per acre, hence reduced planting costs per acre.

2. Whether species is a shade bearer or light demander. Shade bearers can be planted closer than light demanders.

3. Rate of growth in youth. Quicker growth means that the lower branches interlace earlier and canopy is produced earlier, and so can be planted wider.

4. Probable future income from thinnings. If there is little demand for small produce likely to come from first thinnings, then plant wider which means that the trees will be bigger when they require to be thinned.

5. Branch suppression and hence the reduction in the size of knots is achieved earlier by planting closer.

6. On exposed and poor sites plant closer, on good sites plant wider.

Planting distances will vary according to the above factors, but the spacing generally adopted is as follows:—

Scots Pine.............................$4\frac{1}{2}$ to 5 feet apart.

Corsican Pine ....5 to 6 feet apart.

Larches ....6 to 7 feet apart.

Douglas Fir ....6 to 7 feet apart.

Norway Spruce ....5 to 6 feet apart.

Sitka Spruce..........................$5\frac{1}{2}$ to 7 feet apart.

Oak ....plant at 4 ft. by 2 ft., or 4 ft. by 4 ft. The 4 feet refers to distance between rows of plants and 2 feet to distance between plants in the rows.

Beech ....4 feet by 4 feet.

Poplar ....22 feet by 22 feet.

Other hardwoods ....$4\frac{1}{2}$ feet by $4\frac{1}{2}$ feet.

Regularity of Planting. There are several factors in favour of having regular spacing for planting. In the first instance each plant has the same growing space. It is easy to regulate the number of plants required per acre. It is easier to find the small plants when clearing them of weeds

such as bracken, grass, etc. It is easier to fill up gaps due to
deaths. At a later date, by planting at regular spacing, it may
be easier to mark the trees to be removed in the first thinnings.

There are two regular methods of planting, the square
or rectangular, and the triangular. To find the number of
plants required for one acre if using triangular, planting is
as follows:–

There are 43,560 square feet in an acre. Divide 43,560 by
the square of the side of the triangle and multiply by 1·155.

For example, if the side of the triangle is 5 feet, plants
required per acre are:—

$$\frac{43,560}{5 \times 5} \times 1 \cdot 155 = 2012 \text{ plants per acre.}$$

To find the number of plants required for one acre if
using square or rectangular planting, divide 43,560 by the
square of the side, or by the multiple of the sides. If spacing
is to be at 5 feet by 5 feet, then in square planting $\frac{43,560}{5 \times 5}$ or
1742 plants will be required per acre. If the spacing is to be
at 5 feet by 4 feet, then the number of plants required per
acre is $\frac{43,560}{5 \times 4} = 2178$ plants.

General Control of Planting. There are several points
to which the forester must pay particular attention if he is
to have good but cheap results from his planting. If plants
are received from the nursery they should be taken as near
to the planting site as possible and heeled or sheughed in
the ground. Before doing so it is best to cut the strings of
the bundles. If the planting squad is working on piece work,
then the strings should be kept loosely round the bundles
to make counting easier later on when planting. If the
plants arrive in packages during frosty weather, the
packages should be opened and the roots covered with
straw or dead bracken. Tools should be of good quality,
well maintained, and suitable for the type of ground and

method of planting. The plants must be kept in a planting bag or basket, and only one removed at a time for planting. If work stops for more than about a quarter of an hour, the plants should be temporarily sheughed in. Start the squad off under a leader in échelon formation at the correct spacing between rows. Keep the lines straight, erecting an odd sighting post if necessary, and ensure correct spacing between plants in the line. Notches or holes for roots must be deep enough and wide enough to allow the roots to be spread out and not bunched up. In turf planting, the roots must be spread out under the turf. The ground must be firmed carefully by the heel of the planter's boot, ensuring that the plants are not skinned in the firming process. Plant trees vertically and to the correct depth, that is not less than the depth to which the trees had been in the nursery. Good planting can be tested by trying to pull out newly planted trees between thumb and fore-fingers. If there is no movement then planting is satisfactory. Planting must stop in very dry, snowy and frosty weather. A plant may survive bad planting, but it will not survive if its roots are carelessly handled from the time of lifting in the nursery until the time of planting. At all times take care of the roots of the plants. When areas which had previously carried a hardwood crop, such as coppice areas, are being replanted no plant should be put in within a foot of an old stump, otherwise it would be either smothered by the coppice shoots which come up or cut over during the weeding operations.

Manuring after Planting. In exceptional circumstances, such as on poor peat areas, manuring of the young planted trees is justified. This should be done just after planting. About two ounces of Basic Slag or Ground Mineral Phosphate, should be sprinkled round the collar of the plant, or in the case of turf planting the manure may be applied under the turf. The manure will have little effect until the second growing season after planting.

Beating Up. Beating up is the term applied to the

operation of replacing failures in recently planted plantations. All deaths may not occur in the first year after planting, and it is often a saving of money if the beating up is
left until after the second year of growth has passed. It must
be borne in mind that there is no need to have a complete
stocking of trees on the ground. In the case of replanting
hardwood areas, some stool shoots may be allowed to grow
on to take the place of a dead planted tree. If beating up is
left until the second year after planting, this means that the
beat up tree has to be kept clear of weeds after the normal
planting has grown beyond the weed stage, unless bigger
trees are used for the beating up. When weeding of the
plants is being done, a percentage check of the deaths in a
row can be carried out. Try to find the cause of the failure,
and if necessary change the species for beating up, and a
faster growing species may be suitable. It is very wasteful
to fill up blanks caused by the death of one or even two
plants in succession. Where three deaths occur in succession
it will be sufficient to replace by one plant only, properly
spaced.

Weeding. After planting there is very often a strong
growth of herbaceous weeds and grasses. The most common are bracken, bramble, briar and stool shoots of hardwood species, and in many places willow herb may be
abundant. It is essential that all the newly planted trees
should have freedom for growth, and also that there is
no danger of the weed growth dying in the autumn and
burying the young plants as happens with bracken. Where
growth is excessively strong it may be necessary to weed
twice in one season, but in most cases one weeding is
sufficient. Grass hooks or long handled bill hooks are the
best tools, and, in case of accidents, workers should take
alternate rows so that there is a safe distance between each
worker. The plants should be completely relieved of all
competing vegetation, and cleared of all vegetation which
is likely to fall on the plants and bury them. Care must be
taken not to cut the young trees, and the supervisor should

ensure that only sufficient weeding is done to free the plants. Much money can be wasted by excessive weeding to make a very tidy job. Weeding will most likely go on for several years and where there is strong growing vegetation and slow growing plants, weeding may be necessary for up to five years. In other places there may be no necessity for weeding, and although the initial costs of ploughing an area may be high, much money can be saved in weeding.

Drain Maintenance. In all areas, but especially so in high rainfall areas, it is essential that drains must be looked at regularly, and where necessary cleared. It may not be necessary to keep every drain running, as the land may have dried up considerably by the drainage before planting. In the peat areas in particular there will have been some contraction in width and depth, and it may be necessary to keep every drain open. In addition every other drain may be requiring deepening, as it is only by having deep drains that tree roots will penetrate deeply and thus reduce damage and risk of windblow. In areas where there is strong growth of *Molinia* (flying bent or purple moorgrass), this is very liable to blow when it dies off in winter, and is certain to block some drains. This must be carefully watched. All drains must be carefully checked before the lower branches interlace and canopy is formed and the thicket stage of the plantation is reached.

Establishment of Plantations. A plantation may be considered to be established when no further beating up and no further weeding is required. Thereafter all operations may be classed as tending or maintenance of the forest, which is discussed in the next chapter.

CHAPTER IX

TENDING AND THINNING OF PLANTATIONS

We have seen the need for keeping competing weeds clear from the trees which we wish to grow as a crop. When the trees are above the weed growth and from five to ten years old, their rate of height growth usually speeds up. Their side branches grow out and interlace, forming a canopy which will generally smother the ground vegetation. Whilst the trees are growing quickly in the thicket stage, regular inspections must be made through the plantations. It will usually be necessary to cut inspection racks to enable the forester to have access to the interior of the woods. These racks are made by sawing off, close to the stem, the branches of trees in two adjoining rows up to a height of six feet. Depending on the uniformity of the stand, these racks may be spaced at two to four chain intervals.

Brashing. Eventually inspection will show that the dead branches on the trees within the plantation, though not as a rule round its edges, extend to a height of five to six feet from the ground. This is the stage at which the crop is likely to need its first thinning, in order to give the trees more room for development. These lower dead branches are best cut off by using an eighteen inch curved pruning saw, with a two foot or two foot six inch straight handle. Some people prefer to use a long handled pruning chisel, or bill-hook, or for some species like the Larches, a blunt instrument like a pick shaft. The main point is to get a quick clean cut without damaging the bole of the tree. This operation is called "brashing," and much money can be wasted by overdoing the brashing, especially as a fully brashed wood looks much neater than a partially brashed wood. It must be remembered that the purpose of brashing is to allow the forester to get into his woods to mark the thinnings and to enable the forest workers to get in to fell the thinnings. By brashing the fire risk can be reduced, especially if the brashings are removed from road and rides sides. The intensity of brashing on rides sides is governed by the fire risk. Removal of lower branches allows knot free timber to be laid on over a core which has small knots. Fresh air is allowed to circulate through the woods. Brashing can often be done in wet or hard weather, and may be done economically when many other forest operations are not possible. Probably the best intensity of brashing for most species is from 50 to 60 per cent of the trees which are to be left after the first thinning. There is no need to brash those that are to come out in the thinnings, and in some of the hardwood species and with the Larches, fewer trees may be brashed. One can brash the trees in every third row, or brash so as to make a lane between every third and fourth row. After brashing, the forester can get access to his woods to see if any cleaning requires to be done.

Cleaning. Whilst the plantations are in the thicket stage it may be necessary to cut out fast growing weed tree species which are damaging the planted crop, or to remove climbing weeds such as ivy or honeysuckle, or even to remove some of the planted trees which have developed into rough spreading trees and are doing serious damage to good neighbours. Such an operation is called a cleaning, or sometimes called a pre-thinning. It is not generally considered that the produce from a cleaning can be sold, or if it can be sold, that the receipts will cover the costs of the operation.

Types of Trees. During the thicket stage there develops a struggle between the individual trees for light and for food from the soil, with the result that trees develop differently, and may be classified into the following catagories.

Dominant Trees. These are the tallest in the crop, usually the largest and most vigorous, and their crowns are partly free. But there may be "wolf" or "whip" trees amongst the dominant trees, and it is not generally desirable to leave these two types in the crop.

Co-Dominant Trees. These have crowns more shortened than the dominants, but their crowns are well up in the canopy. A proportion of these may be "whips." Apart from the removal of the "whips" early in the thinnings of the plantation, it may be best to retain a good proportion of co-dominants to go on to nearly the final crop, or to leave them in to control the lower branches of the dominant trees.

Sub-Dominant Trees. These are relatively short trees whose crowns are not in the upper canopy. They are useful in controlling the lower branches of the crowns of dominants and co-dominants, and there is no urgency for their removal, unless they start to interfere with the crowns of better trees. They may, in the case of shade-bearing species, develop into a crop tree if the adjoining good trees are damaged by animals, insects, or by climatic factors. In light demanding species the prospect of this development is remote and they should be removed before they die or become diseased.

Suppressed Trees. These are trees which are standing under the shade of the older trees. They seldom have any prospect of recovery, but may do so with certain species, such as Norway Spruce and Silver Fir. Unless they are really in the way or diseased there is no obvious reason to remove them at early thinnings, and they should, where possible, be left to grow into the larger sizes before being removed. Where they are hopelessly suppressed they should be removed.

Dead and Dying Trees. This includes broken, bent and leaning trees. They may assist in the spread of insect of fungal attacks, and they are generally removed at each thinning, if possible before they die.

"Wolf" Trees. A "wolf" tree may be described as a vigorous growing tree but with a mis-shapen large crown

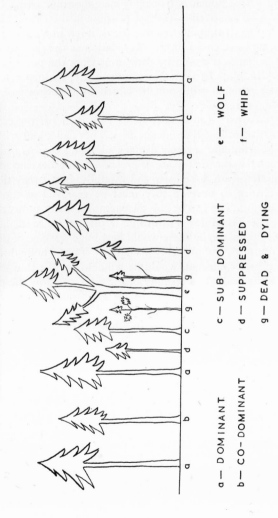

DIAGRAMMATIC ILLUSTRATION OF TREE TYPES

a — DOMINANT

b — CO-DOMINANT

c — SUB-DOMINANT

d — SUPPRESSED

g — DEAD & DYING

e — WOLF

f — WHIP

and coarse rough branching, often with a crooked stem, and a tree which is damaging neighbouring trees. These must be removed as early as possible in the cleaning, pre-thinning or thinning operations, as, if left in the crop, they would have to go on for the rotation as the gap made by their removal would be dangerous from the point of risk of windblow. If they are removed early, the gap made by their removal will soon be closed by branches from adjoining trees.

"Whips." Tall slender stems with their narrow crowns mainly in the sub-dominant class. They flail about with the least wind and severely damage adjoining crowns of good trees. In the first place they should not develop if the thinnings are done early and carefully, but if they do get a chance to develop they must be removed at the next thinning. The gap left by their removal is not noticeable.

The Need for Thinning. If plantations were left to develop naturally there would be a huge wastage of potential timber, and probably plantations, if not wholly diseased and insect infected, would be windblown. We thin woods for the health and stability of the crop, to allow the better trees more light and soil space for proper development. In mixed woods the forester can favour the stems which he wishes to develop by judicious thinning. Apart from first thinnings, there is usually a credit balance of income over expenditure on the operation, giving some early return for the costs involved in establishment and maintenance of the woods. If plantations are left unthinned, the proportion of live crown to total height gives an indication as to the need for thinning. The proportion of live crown to total height should be about one third.

Grades and Frequency of Thinnings. Thinning of plantations is one of the most controversial branches of forestry. There is a school of foresters who believe in thinning heavily, and others who believe in thinning lightly. One thing is certain, that one cannot lay down on paper what should be done in every plantation. Thinnings differ with species, and within species differ with locality. There are some fundamental facts that can be stated. It does not matter how dense or open a wood is kept, there is little variation in height growth. The more open the wood the quicker is girth put on the trees remaining in the stand. It does not matter what grade of thinning a wood receives, the total volume of timber produced in one rotation does not vary to any great extent. In lightly thinned woods this volume is spread over a large number of small stems, whereas in heavily thinned woods the volume is derived from a small number of larger and more valuable stems.

Light Grade, B Grade. This grade is not often used unless it can be carried out at short intervals, and then only used with slow growing species, or at first thinning. There is no break in the overhead canopy. The trees removed would include: dead, suppressed, some sub-dominants and "whips." Occasional "wolf" trees would be removed so long as no large breaks were made in the canopy.

Moderate Grade, C Grade. The result of a moderate grade thinning is that about four fifths of the sky will be shut out. The crowns of the dominants will be more or less in contact with each other. Trees removed include:— dead, dying, suppressed, whips, some co-dominants to allow for the development of adjoining dominants.

Moderate Heavy Grade Low Thinning, C/D Grade. This is the normal thinning grade for conifers except Larches. In this grade of thinning the following tree types are removed:—dead, dying, suppressed, whips, some co-dominants, and some of the dominants where their crowns are in close contact. About one quarter of sky is visible from below.

Heavy Low Thinning, D Grade. This grade of thinning involves considerable breaking of the canopy, so that about one third of sky is visible from below, with the result that most of the dominants and some of the co-dominants will have completely free crowns, but gaps should not be so large that they will not close over before the next thinning is due. This interval between thinnings is usually from three to four years when the plantations are young to middle aged. This grade is used mainly for Larches, but could be used for the quick growing light demanders.

Other grades, such as the very heavy low thinning (E Grade), the light crown (L.C.) grade, and heavy crown thinning (H.C.) grade, are occasionally used, but mainly for experimental purposes.

Choice of Thinnings Grade. The grade of thinning for any species in any plantation cannot be laid down as a hard and fast rule. The grade to be used will depend on consideration of such facts as:—Age, height, rate of growth, exposure, possible markets, etc. The frequency with which woods are thinned will also depend on the species, rate of growth, and other site factors. In the notes which follow on the individual tree species, the normal grades and frequencies are given, but they may be varied according to local circumstances. The quality of timber depends on the regularity of the growth of the tree. If trees are kept close, the annual rings are close, if kept open then there will be wide rings. The aim should be to thin the woods so that the annual rings are regular, and not varying in width.

Marking of Thinnings. This is best done by two people, one to mark the trees to be removed, and the other to judge the trees which should be removed. The forester will always look at the crowns of the trees first, so that he may allow for the development of crowns of the best formed trees and remove individuals which are interfering with the crowns of good trees. Whilst the marking of thinnings is in progress the forester should also consider the removal of trees here and there in order to develop lanes for the extraction of the thinnings. The trees to be removed are first, *"blazed,"* that is a strip of bark is cut off with axe, bill-hook or slasher, to expose the white wood below. This makes a good, easily seen, mark; two such blazes should be made on each tree, on opposite sides of it. If, however, a forester is new to the craft of thinning he may wish to mark the trees to be removed with white paint, so that he may reconsider his judgment, or bring in an expert to advise on the work. Again he may wish to decide on which trees should be left to go on to the final crop. He may mark these with paint, and remove only those trees which are interfering with the development of his selected final crop trees. The forester will also consider the spacing of his crop, so that full use is being made of the soil, and to ensure that full advantage is taken of all factors affecting growth and stability of the trees.

In the notes on the treatment of the individual species, the relationship between top height (average height of 100 largest trees per acre) of crops to the spacing distance between trees is given as mathematical fractions. Although these may not be strictly adhered to, they are very good average relationships for the species at all times of the rotation.

Damage during Thinnings. The damage which can be done to trees left standing, due to careless workmanship, can be subdivided into two categories.

(a) Damage due to felling and extraction of thinnings. In the felling of trees being removed in the thinning, it is best, as far as possible, to throw all the trees in one direction, either with their butts or their tops in the direction of extraction. It is almost certain that some trees will hang in the crowns of other trees, but care must be taken to ensure that the stems of trees to be left standing are not scarred and wounded to cause blemishes in the timber, and allow the possible entry of fungal diseases. Before extraction starts it is well to drive stakes, about four feet long, into the ground close to the butts of trees left standing on the sides of extraction lanes. When the thinned poles are being removed they will bump against these stakes, but will not damage the butts of the trees. Brashings cleared from extraction lanes may be piled against the butts of standing trees to act as a buffer against damage when extracting.

(b) Damage to drains due to felling and extraction of

thinnings. Before extraction of thinnings begins, small bridges made from the tops of the trees removed in the thinnings should be put across all drains on the extraction lanes. After the trees have been felled and the thinnings removed, the drains in the wood must be gone over to ensure that there are no blockages due to branches from the fellings, or due to the extraction. All blockages should be cleared and drains deepened where necessary, to ensure the stability of the crop after thinning. Extensive use of drag paths on steep slopes in high rainfall areas may cause these paths to develop into water channels, and care must be taken to prevent erosion.

Thinning of Individual Tree Species

Scots Pine. Not very fast growing tree, but moderately strong light demander. Trees once suppressed, have little power of recovery even if given room and light to develop. Wolf trees likely to develop, especially where damage is done by the Pine Shoot Moth. Start thinning when the top height is about 25 feet. Thinnings should be on a moderate grade to start with, then on to moderate heavy grade. The interval between thinnings should be four or five years. The spacing of trees in the plantation should be about one fifth of the top height.

Corsican Pine. Moderately fast grower, but will tolerate more shade than Scots Pine. Wolf trees not likely to develop. Start thinning when top height is 25 to 30 feet. Thin on a moderate scale throughout with intervals of four to five years between thinnings. The spacing of trees should be about $\frac{1}{5 \cdot 5}$ of the top height.

Lodgepole Pine. Not many pure plantations of any size usually planted of this species. It is a moderately fast grower, and moderate to strong light demander. Not many wolf trees likely to develop with good strains. Start thinning when about 25 feet in height and thin to a moderate grade. May require thinning every three or four years, depending on the site factor, and therefore rate of growth. The spacing should be about one-fifth of top height.

Note. All thinnings of Pines, if they are not to be removed immediately, should have the bark peeled off in order to reduce the breeding ground of the Pine Beetle.

European Larch. Fast growing tree, intolerant of shade. Suppressed trees never likely to recover even if given light. Whips likely to develop if unthinned. Liable to fungus attack causing canker on stems. Must have fresh air throughout the plantations. Start thinning early when height about 25 feet, thin to a heavy grade, and thin frequently. Usual interval between thinnings is three years, and spacing between trees should be about $\frac{1}{4.5}$ of the height.

Japanese Larch. Very fast growing tree, especially in early life. Less tolerant of shade than European Larch. Wolves and Whips will develop if thinning is delayed, and suppressed trees unlikely to recover. Start thinning early, about 12th to 15th year (top height 25–30 feet), thin heavy, breaking canopy, and thin frequently. Usual interval between thinnings is 3 years. Spacing should be about $\frac{1}{4.5}$ of top height.

Hybrid Larch. Should be treated as Japanese Larch.

Douglas Fir. Quick growing tree. Tolerant of shade. Wolf trees likely to develop. Liable to windthrow. Suppressed trees will respond to thinning. Start early (top height about 30 feet) and thin to a moderate grade, but remove wolf trees early, leaving sub-dominants to fill the gap if necessary, as they will respond. Thin every three years on a moderate heavy grade. Spacing should be about $\frac{1}{5.5}$ of the top height.

Norway Spruce. Moderately fast grower, tolerant of shade. Wolf trees and whips not likely to develop. Not very windfirm. Start thinning when top height about 30 feet, on a moderate grade, and continue on this grade with thinnings at five year intervals. Suppressed trees will recover. Spacing should be one sixth of the height.

Sitka Spruce. Very fast grower, not very tolerant of shade. Wolf trees likely to develop from damaged strong growing trees. Liable to windthrow. Start thinning early, when top height is about 30 feet, and thin on a moderate to heavy grade every three years. Suppressed trees do not usually recover to any great extent. Spacing should be about one sixth of the top height.

Omorika or Servian Spruce. Moderately slow grower, shade bearing species. Wolf trees and whips are not likely to develop. Treat as Norway Spruce.

Other Conifer Species. Not generally planted on a large scale. Thinnings should start when top height is about 30 feet, and should be on a moderate to moderately heavy grade depending on the rate of growth. They are mostly shade bearing species, and liable to windblow on wet or moist areas, and may require thinning about every four years to maintain stability. At present not enough data available.

Broadleaved Species.

Oak. Slow growing species in early life, and strong light demander. Liable to develop a wide crown if too open and wolf trees are often numerous. Windfirm. Too much light allows dormant buds lower down the stem to develop epicormic shoots and spoil the cleanness of the timber. Again if kept too dense these epicormic shoots may develop. Whips are likely to develop if kept too dense. Keep crop fairly dense in early life. Start thinning when the top height is about 30 feet, but thin lightly, removing whips and wolves early. Further thinning at five year intervals on a moderate scale, and later in life at ten year intervals. Spacing at about one-fifth of the height in early half of the rotation to about one quarter of height in later life.

Beech. Rate of growth depends on site and varies considerably over the country. It has a tendency to fork with certain strains. Strong shade bearer, and suppressed trees will recover when given light. Windfirm. Start thinning on a light grade when top height is about 30 feet. Subsequent thinnings at five year intervals on a moderate grade and more heavy when about sixty years old. Spacing about one sixth of height in the young stage, but down to one quarter when middle aged to old.

Ash. Quick grower on good sites, and fairly strong light demander. Whips likely to develop if kept close. Often has leading bud damaged by frost or Ash Bud Moth, and side branches will develop, causing forking. The aim should be to get good quick grown timber by thinning early. Start when top height is 25–30 feet and thin on a moderately heavy scale, taking out whips and wolves. Continue on this scale every three to four years, then give plenty growing space to the selected final crop stems. In growing quality Ash for sports goods, a short rotation may be best, keeping the stems slightly denser to get clean boles of over 20 feet, then opening out to allow the trees to develop. Regular width of annual rings is important. Where two leaders develop after the leading bud has been damaged, one of the leaders should be pruned off.

Sycamore. Not planted pure on any large scale. Will tolerate moderate shade. Fairly quick grower on good sites. Liable to fork like Ash, and may need pruning. Thin moderately to start with, and then heavy when good straight clean bole of about 20 to 25 feet has been attained. Clean straight timber is valuable for veneers, and this should be the aim throughout the treatment of Sycamore plantations. Grey squirrels are particularly attracted to Sycamore, and cause serious damage by bark peeling.

Sweet Chestnut. Generally grown as coppice crops.

Poplars. Planted very wide initially. Remove poorly developed trees. Prune where necessary, possibly every year. Keep crowns free at all times as damaged crowns will not recover. Probably one thinning required.

Birch. Moderately slow grower and light demander. Remove mis-shapen trees. Suppressed trees do not recover. Thin on a light to moderate scale where plantations are available.

Lime. Coppices well, and if strong shoots appear where felling has taken place, keep the stool shoots close (about 20 stems per stool) until 40 to 50 feet in height, then open out until about four shoots per stool. This way it gives good clean timber. Not usually planted pure on any large scale.

Other Broadleaved Species. Not generally planted pure on any large scale, and not much practical information about them available. Always study the development of the crowns and give them growing space as required.

Where Thinnings have been Delayed. In all cases and with all species where thinnings have been delayed, start with a light grade and thin at more frequent intervals. The drainage system should always be checked to reduce the risk from windblow.

High Pruning. Pruning is generally not worth the costs, except where there is a higher price available for quality timber. It may be justified on conifers where about 100 stems per acre are pruned to 20 feet in height, but this should be done before the diameter is more than four inches. Pruning of hardwoods is justified where quality timber is more valuable for veneers, furniture, etc.

CHAPTER X

MEASUREMENT OF FOREST PRODUCE AND STANDING CROPS

Felled trees and forest produce are measured for record purposes, sale purposes, operation costs and for determining yields from plantations. We must first determine according to sale possibility, what is to be measured. This will depend on the general shape of the tree, where heavy branches come off giving reduced girth, and generally on the taper of the tree. It must be borne in mind that when a tree is measured in sections this usually gives a bigger volume than when a tree is measured as a whole.

There can be no hard and fast rule as to what is to be measured as timber, but generally in conifers it is taken down to 3 inches in diameter and down to 6 inches diameter for hardwoods. Generally, conifers are measured as a whole, and hardwoods in sections because of their more branching habit.

Quarter Girth Volume. In Britain the unit of measurement is the Quarter Girth Cubic foot. In this system the sectional area of the middle of the tree or log is obtained by squaring a quarter of the circumference or girth, and is expressed as $\left(\dfrac{G}{4}\right)^2$. If we assume that a tree tapers evenly throughout its length, the sectional area at mid length is approximately equal to half the sum of the end sectional areas. In practice this sectional area gives a reasonably accurate measure of the tree's cubic contents. The volume of the tree is then obtained by measuring the length of the tree and the circumference or quarter girth at its mid length, and calculated from the following formula if the girth is taken in inches.

Volume of Tree in Cubic Feet Quarter Girth

$$= \frac{\left(\dfrac{G}{4}\right)^2 \times \text{length in ft.}}{144}$$

or Hoppus Feet.

Special tapes are available so that the Quarter Girth is read off immediately, and special tables (Called Hoppus Tables) are available so that for any Quarter Girth and any length in feet or fractions of feet the Volume can be immediately read off in Hoppus Feet. Alternatively, the method shown in Appendix 6 may be used.

A Hoppus Foot is the solid contents of a block one foot long and having a quarter girth of one foot.

True Volume. If instead of measuring the quarter girth at mid length of the tree we measure the girth or diameter at mid length of the tree, and from this measurement we calculate the mid length sectional area, we would get the true sectional area. This true sectional area multiplied by the length would give the true volume and this would be greater than the quarter girth volume. This would be expressed in cubic feet.

Relationship between True and Quarter Girth Volume.

True Volume = Quarter Girth Volume Plus 27½ per cent
         or = Quarter Girth Volume × 1·273.
Quarter Girth Volume = True Volume minus 21½ per cent
         or = True Volume × ·785.

Volumes of Trees and Logs. The volume of trees and logs is found by measuring the full length in feet by tape, then finding the quarter girth by tape at half this length. By referring to the Hoppus Decimal Tables, for the measured Quarter Girth and length, the Volume can be immediately read off in cubic feet. If this measurement is for a sale, then it should be stated that the quarter girth system was used.

Bark Allowances. In Britain all measurements of trees and logs are taken over bark and this must be stated during any sale negotiations. Bark allowances are variable, but a general guide.

Measurement of Round Stakes, Pitprops and Poles

The measurement of these is taken from length and diameter at the small end, but the diameter is taken under bark. A small set of tables has been prepared for measuring such types of produce, called Smith's Pitprop Tables. There is therefore no need to calculate the volume of such produce, but merely to measure length and top diameter under bark and refer to these tables to read off the volume. Again it must be stated that such tables have been used to determine the volumes, and the volume will be in Hoppus feet.

Cordwood. Rough branches of hardwoods are often cut to length and piled for sale. A general size used is to cut the branches in four feet lengths and make a pile of these lengths, eight feet long and four feet high. That pile known as a cord contains 128 cubic feet including the air spaces, but the timber must be piled as closely as possible.

Long Poles in Stacked Measure. Long poles, such as are obtained from first thinnings, may be piled with butt ends all one way, ready for crosscutting into pitprops and the forester may wish to get an estimate of the volume of timber in the pile. This estimate can be got by multiplying the average length, by average breadth, by the average height of the pile by 1/3. This is only an estimate, but is fairly accurate, and allows for air spaces between poles.

Measurement of Sawn Timber. Sawn timber is usually stacked according to size of cross-section, e.g. 6″ × 3″, 5″ × 2½″, etc., and is usually stacked according to length. The method of measurement of sawn timber is to count the number of pieces of each cross-section, and multiply this number by the length of each piece, giving the total lineal run of that cross-section. By reference to one of the many sets of volume tables, such as the Cube Calculator, the volume can be read off. Alternatively, by multiplying the lineal run in feet by the cross-section in square inches, and dividing the result by 144, one can find the volume in true cubic feet.

Losses in Conversion. When converting long poles, such as are obtained from first and second thinnings, into pit props etc., there is an actual and an artificial loss. The actual loss is brought by the loss of sawdust and odd offcuts which are not measured. This loss will amount to 15 per cent or 10 per cent of the input to the sawbench. The artificial loss is brought about by bad stacking or sorting into sizes of the props which are produced. Orders for props are based on length and minimum top diameter under bark. Crosscutting to length is usually done fairly accurately, but stacking is usually on the generous side. This can be partly avoided by ensuring that there is a fairly wide variety of sizes to cut to, and also by careful supervision and checking of the prepared piles of props.

If the estate has a small sawmill and is converting some round produce into battens and boards, then the first factor which comes into the calculations of loss in conversion, is the fact that the input to the mill is measured by Quarter Girth Volume, but the output is in True Volume. Therefore before any input and output is made, the input volumes must be brought to true volumes first. The actual losses in conversion may be from 25 per cent to 35 per cent, depending on (a) Quality of timber being sawn, twisted or straight. (b) Range of sizes being cut. There may not be enough sizes to give full utilisation of the log. (c) Type of saw used. The inserted tooth saw, whilst having many advantages over a plate saw, makes a very wide saw cut and is therefore very wasteful.

Measurement of a Standing Tree

Height Measurement. An ocular estimate of the height may be got by placing a staff of known length, say six feet, against the butt of the tree, and standing in a position so that the top and base of the tree are visible, and estimating how often it would be necessary to move the staff to reach the top or timber height of the tree. The product of this number multiplied by the length of the staff will give an estimate of the height of the tree.

By Alloy Rods. Light sectional alloy rods which fit together like a fishing rod may be used to find the heights of trees up to about eighty feet. The rods are fixed together and pushed up through the branches until they stretch to the top of the tree. By adding the lengths of the sections used the height of the tree is found.

By Hypsometers. A Hypsometer is an instrument for finding the height of a tree or building etc. Various types may be bought, such as, Christen's, Weise's, Simplex, Altmeter Haga, Blumé Leiss, but Christen's may be made from a piece of metal or timber.

To make a Christen's Hypsometer, take a piece of wood, with projecting upper and lower ends and having a length of 15 inches between these projections. For use with a rod of 10 feet, mark 10 at A on the piece of timber, then

5	in. from A towards B mark						15 ft. on the timber			
7·5	,,	,,	,,	,,	,,	,,	20 ,,	,,	,,	,,
9	,,	,,	,,	,,	,,	,,	25 ,,	,,	,,	,,
10	,,	,,	,,	,,	,,	,,	30 ,,	,,	,,	,,
10·7	,,	,,	,,	,,	,,	,,	35 ,,	,,	,,	,,
11·25	,,	,,	,,	,,	,,	,,	40 ,,	,,	,,	,,
11·66	,,	,,	,,	,,	,,	,,	45 ,,	,,	,,	,,
12	,,	,,	,,	,,	,,	,,	50 ,,	,,	,,	,,
12·25	,,	,,	,,	,,	,,	,,	55 ,,	,,	,,	,,
12·5	,,	,,	,,	,,	,,	,,	60 ,,	,,	,,	,,
12·8	,,	,,	,,	,,	,,	,,	70 ,,	,,	,,	,,
13·1	,,	,,	,,	,,	,,	,,	80 ,,	,,	,,	,,
13·3	,,	,,	,,	,,	,,	,,	90 ,,	,,	,,	,,
13·5	,,	,,	,,	,,	,,	,,	100 ,,	,,	,,	,,

To use Christen's Hypsometer, set a rod of length 10 feet against the base of the tree to be measured. Walk away from

E

the tree, holding the Hypsometer as a pendulum, until the line of sight through D (in the following figure) to the top of the tree and through E to the butt of the tree coincide. Then the line of sight from the eye to the top of the staff against the tree cuts the Hypsometer at the height of the tree.

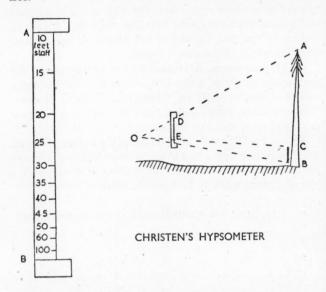

CHRISTEN'S HYPSOMETER

Weise's Hypsometer. This consists of a tube with an objective in the shape of a cross at one end and an eyepiece at the other. The height scale is fastened along the upper side of the tube. It has a zero point some distance from the end and is graduated in both directions from this zero point. A second scale, known as the distance scale, is inserted at the zero point of the height scale and moves up and down at right angles to the height scale. From the upper or zero point of the distance scale is suspended a plumb rod with a sharp inner edge. Both scales are graduated in units of the same dimension.

In using the instrument, the horizontal distance from the tree to a point where the top and bottom of the tree are visible, is measured, and the distance scale is set at the equivalent number of units, either feet or yards. The instrument is then directed to the top of the tree, inclined slightly to the left so that the plumb rod hangs free. With

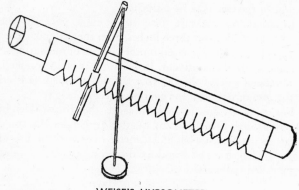

WEISE'S HYPSOMETER

the intersection of the cross wires of the objective directed on the top or on the timber height of the tree, the instrument is turned gently to the right, so that the edge of the plumb rod is caught in a notch of the height scale. The reading opposite this notch then gives the height of the tree above the eye in the units chosen (feet or yards). The length of the tree below the eye is determined in a similar manner by directing the instrument on the foot of the tree. The total height is got by adding the two readings. Should the observer be below the level of the foot of the tree, both readings will be on the same side of the zero point on the height scale, and then the second reading must be deducted from the first to get the height of the tree. As the horizontal distance from the observer to the tree must be measured, the instrument is not very suitable for steep slopes, and in such places should be used across the slope.

Girth Measurement. Having found the height of the tree we must consider how to find the other factors of volume determination. A tree does not grow in the form of a cylinder, nor does it grow in the shape of a cone. But for rough estimates of volume a tree is considered to have an even taper, therefore if the girth near the ground can be measured, by deduction for even taper, the girth at the mid height of the tree may be estimated.

In Britain we measure the girth or more generally the quarter girth at 4 feet three inches from the ground, called Breast Height. This is based on the custom of measuring at 1·3 metres on the continent. In Britain it is often accepted, as a general rule of thumb, that the quarter girth falls off at the rate of one inch for every ten feet in height.

For rough estimates we measure the Breast Height Quarter Girth Over Bark by quarter girth tape. We could measure the Breast Height Diameter over bark by use of two parallel pieces of wood fixed on a measuring wooden scale called Callipers.

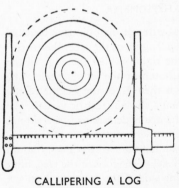

CALLIPERING A LOG

Having measured the height of the tree, we determine half height. We then deduct one inch in diameter or quarter girth for every ten feet between breast height and mid height, and thus find the mid height diameter or quarter girth. By use of the Hoppus Tables for this mid height quarter girth and total or timber height of the tree, the volume of the tree can be read off. If Hoppus tables are not available the mid height sectional area can be calculated and when multiplied by the total or timber height of the tree will give the volume of the tree.

For Example:—A tree has a timber height of 48 feet, and a breast height quarter girth over bark of 6 inches. Its mid timber height will be 24 feet. There is a rise of approximately twenty feet from breast height to mid timber height, therefore there is a fall of 2 inches in quarter girth (1 inch in 10 feet), and therefore the mid height quarter girth will be 4 inches over bark. We then look up the Hoppus tables for 4 inch quarter girth and length of 48 feet and read off the volume of timber in the tree and describe it as cubic feet over bark Hoppus measure.

If we wish a more accurate measurement of the volume then we must get a more accurate measurement for the mid height quarter girth, and this can only be got by climbing the tree to mid height and measuring the quarter girth at that point. Again from Hoppus tables we can read off the volume corresponding to the mid height quarter girth and height.

If a very accurate measurement of a specimen tree is desired it must be measured in sections of say ten feet, and by climbing to measure the quarter girths at various fixed heights. The volume of the first 10 feet can be got by measuring the quarter girth at 5 feet, and finding the volume from the tables for this 10 feet section. The volume for the next 10 feet can be found by climbing and measuring the quarter girth at 15 feet, and by using this figure in the Hoppus tables for a length of 10 feet we get the volume of the section between 10 and 20 feet in height. This is continued up the stem until the whole tree is measured in sections of 10 feet and the total obtained by addition.

By Use of Form Factor. The Form Factor of a tree is the relationship which the volume of a tree bears to the volume of a cylinder of the same height and same sectional area at breast height. Form Factors have been calculated for various species at various ages and are published in the Yield Tables produced by the Forestry Commission. Therefore if we wish to find the volume of a tree in a wood, and we know the age of the tree and measure the height of the tree, we can find the Form Factor for that tree by reference to these Yield Tables. The volume of the tree is then found from the formula:—Volume of Tree = Height × Sectional Area at Breast Height × Form Factor.

This gives a fairly accurate volume for a tree in a plantation.

Measurement of Volumes of Woods

Complete Enumeration. This is only necessary when a very accurate volume is required, or where the wood is old, or of uneven age and growth, and where it is not possible to take samples. This is not used in regular stands of even aged woods. All trees are girthed or callipered at breast height and entered in their girth classes. The volume of one tree in each girth class is found by either felling and measuring, or by either of the aforementioned methods of finding the volume of a standing tree. This volume multiplied by the number of trees in the class, gives the volume for the class, and the total of all the classes gives the volume of timber in the wood.

A team of four is most suitable, one booking and three measuring. The wood may be divided off in strips by the use of stakes or surveyors ranging poles. After measuring the girth or diameter of the tree it is best to mark the tree by scribe or chalk to ensure that it is not measured twice. The person booking should record by the gate method. A sample field book might be as that shown opposite.

Sampling Procedure. It is often impracticable to measure whole woods, and unnecessary in even aged woods. Some system of sampling is therefore resorted to. In sampling, a smaller number of trees, as representative of the crop as possible, are measured. There must be no bias in the selection of the samples, with no edge trees and no large blanks included in the sample. Sampling may be done either at random or systematically. If done at random, plots are usually larger in area, and in all cases enough area is measured to give a 10 per cent sample.

Breast Height ¼ Girth Over Bark Inches	Enumeration	No. of Trees in Class	Height of sample tree in class in feet	Volume of sample tree in class Cubic Feet	Total Volume of Class Cubic Feet
4	III	5	44	1·2	6·0
4¼	III	3	44	1·52	4·56
4½	卌 II	7	44	2·3	16·1
4¾	卌 卌 III	13	46	2·8	36·4
5	卌 卌 III	13	48	3·0	39·0
5¼	卌 卌 卌 I	16	48	3·5	56·0
5½	卌 卌 卌 IIII	19	48	4·1	77·9
5¾	卌 卌 卌 卌 III	23	50	4·9	112·7
6	卌 卌 卌 卌 I	21	50	5·5	115·5
6¼	卌 卌 卌 III	18	50	6·3	113·4
6½	卌 卌 卌	15	48	6·7	100·5
6¾	卌 卌 卌 I	16	48	7·5	120·0
7	卌 卌 III	13	48	8·3	107·9
7¼	卌 卌	10	48	9·2	92·0
7½	卌	5	48	10·0	50·0
7¾	III	3	48	11·0	33·0
8	I	1	48	12·0	12·0

Total Volume of crop = 1092·96 cubic feet.

Systematic Sampling.

(1) **Percentage of Trees.** Count all the trees, but girth only every tenth tree. Record by the gate system in the field book. In mixtures keep the species separate.

(2) **Percentage of rows.** Every tree in every tenth row is measured, but the measurements should not start with the first row which is an edge row as the trees are likely to be larger in this row. Measure the 3rd, 13th, 23rd lines, etc. Record the girth measurements in the girth classes by the gate method—again in mixtures keeping the species separate.

(3) **Regularly Spaced Strips.** Strips half a chain wide at intervals of five chains, or strips one chain wide at intervals of 10 chains can be laid out. Every tree in each strip is

again girthed and recorded in the girth classes by the gate system. The measurements for each strip are kept separate.

(4) **Regularly Spaced Plots.** On fairly even country regularly spaced plots can be easily laid out. Starting about one chain in from the edge of the wood, a row of plots can be laid down with the plots every 100 to 200 yards apart. These plots can be either circular, square, rectangular, or triangular in shape, and are usually of one-tenth acre in area. For an equal area the circular plot has less perimeter and therefore is likely to have less trees on the perimeter which may or may not be included in the volume determination and would give variation in volumes. To lay out a tenth circular acre plot, the radius is 37 feet 3 inches. A square plot of one tenth acre has a side of one chain, a triangular plot has a base of 2 chains and a perpendicular height of one chain.

In all these types of plots all trees within the plots are girthed at breast height and recorded in the field book as before.

Determination of Average Sample Trees. In all of these sampling systems described we have to determine from the field book entries the average sample tree. This can be done in two ways.

(a) **By Weise's 40 per cent Rule.** All the trees which have been girthed are added. Forty per cent of this total is calculated. Starting from the highest quarter girth, count back the totals of the trees until this 40 per cent number is reached. This gives the quarter girth of the average tree. This method should not be used for calculations where great accuracy is required. The following is an example of the determination of the average tree by Weise's 40 per cent rule from data shown in the field book opposite.

Start from the 11 inch quarter girth and count backwards until the 60th tree is reached, and it lies in the 8 inch class. That is, the average tree by this method, is a tree of 8 inches quarter girth at breast height.

Breast Height Quarter Girth in Inches	Enumeration	Number of Trees in each girth class
5	Tℋℋ Tℋℋ Tℋℋ Tℋℋ	20
6	Tℋℋ Tℋℋ Tℋℋ Tℋℋ Tℋℋ	25
7	Tℋℋ Tℋℋ Tℋℋ Tℋℋ Tℋℋ Tℋℋ	30
8	Tℋℋ Tℋℋ Tℋℋ Tℋℋ Tℋℋ Tℋℋ	30
9	Tℋℋ Tℋℋ Tℋℋ Tℋℋ Tℋℋ	25
10	Tℋℋ Tℋℋ Tℋℋ	15
11	Tℋℋ	5

Total Number of Trees Girthed   150
40 per cent of this number   = 60

(b) **By Arithmetic Mean Sample Tree.** All trees having been girthed and booked in their classes, the basal area (or cross sectional area at breast height) in square feet is then calculated for each class, and the total basal area of the sample measured is found by addition. This total basal area for the sample is divided by the number of trees girthed in the sample and the result is the basal area of the mean sample tree. To get the basal areas for each quarter girth class is laborious by multiplication, but fortunately decimal Hoppus Tables can again be used to read off the basal area. Look up the appropriate quarter girth table and instead of length in feet, substitute number of trees, and read off the number of cubic feet given in the tables, but for basal area purposes it is called square feet.

Calculation of Volumes in Samples from the Average Sample Tree

Having girthed all the trees in the samples and found the average sample tree by either of the two methods just described, we must find the volume of these average trees. For the accuracy required by using the Weise's 40 per cent rule, the volume of the average tree can be found by any of the methods described for finding the height of a standing

E*

tree. Having found the volume of the average tree the total volume of the sample can be got by multiplying this volume by the total number of trees in the sample.

For Example. In a tenth acre plot, 34 trees were girthed, The girth of the average tree was found by Weise's rule to be 7″. The volume of this tree was measured and found to be 9 cubic feet. Therefore the volume of the plot was 34 × 9 or 306 cubic feet, and the volume per acre would be 3060 cubic feet.

and

A strip of wood was measured, and the average tree was found by The Arithmetic Mean method as follows:—

Breast Height Quarter Girth Over Bark In inches	Enumeration	Number of Trees	Basal Area in Square Feet
5	⊩⊣ ⊩⊣ III	13	2·257
5½	⊩⊣ ⊩⊣ ⊩⊣ ⊩⊣ II	22	4·621
6	⊩⊣ ⊩⊣ ⊩⊣ ⊩⊣ ⊩⊣	25	6·250
6½	⊩⊣ ⊩⊣ ⊩⊣ ⊩⊣ ⊩⊣ ⊩⊣	30	8·802
7	⊩⊣ ⊩⊣ ⊩⊣ ⊩⊣ III	23	7·826
7½	⊩⊣ ⊩⊣ ⊩⊣ III	18	7·031
8	⊩⊣ ⊩⊣ III	13	5·778
8½	⊩⊣ III	8	4·014
9	⊩⊣	5	2·813
	Totals	157	49·392

The Arithmetic Mean Sample Tree has a Basal Area of

$$\frac{49\cdot392}{157} = \cdot314 \text{ square feet.}$$

This ·314 square feet is equivalent to a Breast Height Quarter Girth Over Bark of 6¾ inches. Three samples trees were found near this quarter girth and their volumes measured accurately.

Sample Trees Measured.

Breast Height Quarter Girth Over Bark in Inches	Basal Area in Square Feet	Heights in Feet	Volume in Cubic Feet
7	·340	50	8·01
7	·340	50	8·01
6½	·293	48	6·64
Totals	·973		22·66

The Volume of timber in the strip

$$= \frac{\text{Volume of Sample Trees} \times \text{Basal Area in strip}}{\text{Basal Area of Sample Trees}}$$

$$= \frac{22 \cdot 66 \times 49 \cdot 392}{\cdot 973} \text{ cubic feet.}$$

$$= 1119 \cdot 22 \text{ cubic feet.}$$

To summarise the methods of measuring the volume of timber in a wood. When a very accurate measurement is required, or where the wood is old and has relatively few trees per acre, or where the wood is of uneven age or growth, then girth every tree at breast height and record in the field book. Measure the standing volume of one tree in each girth class. Find the total volume in each girth class, and then by addition the total volume of the wood.

If an accurate estimate is required, then a 10 per cent sample may be measured. This is used in even aged and even grown woods. Decide on the method of sampling, whether percentage of trees, percentage of rows, regularly spaced strips, regularly spaced plots of square, rectangular, circular or triangular outline. Girth all the trees in the selected sample, and record in girth classes in the field book. Find the average tree in the sample by Weise's 40 per cent rule, or by the Arithmetic Mean Sample Tree method. Find the standing volume of this average sample tree, and by multiplication calculate the volume of the selected sample. From this sample plot volume, calculate the volume of the whole wood.

General Volume Tables. General Volume Tables have been prepared by the Forestry Commission for most forest tree species in Britain. They can be used to find the volume of an average tree, but not the volume of an isolated tree. Therefore measurement of samples, when the average tree in the sample has been found either by Weise's 40 per cent Rule or by the Arithmetic Mean method, we get the breast height quarter girth over bark of the average tree. The height of this average tree is measured, and by reference to the General Volume Tables for that species, for that quarter girth and height, the volume of this tree can be read off.

Increment of Woods. If we wish to determine the increment of woods, this can be done by periodic Inventories or measurements. The volume of the woods are measured at intervals of say five years, and the increment can be found from the formula:–

Increment = (Volume at end of period — Volume at
            Start of period) + Volume removed in
            thinnings.

Valuation of Woodlands. In young woods, up to thinning stage, the value of a plantation is normally found by adding costs of establishment and maintenance and computing at $2\frac{1}{2}$ per cent Compound Interest for the periods involved. In older woods, the standing timber is usually valued. That is, the standing volume is determined and a price per cubic foot fixed. For Example:—A wood contains 4000 cubic feet per acre, and the estimated value is 2/- per cubic foot, then the value per acre of the wood is £400.

CHAPTER XI

PROTECTION OF WOODLANDS AGAINST DAMAGE BY ANIMALS, FIRE, INSECTS AND FUNGI

Animals

In Chapter 4 the various types of fences for the exclusion of stock and animals were described. A very great amount of damage can be done in a very short time by a very few wild animals, such as rabbits, hares, deer and squirrels, especially to young woodlands. These animals must be vigorously controlled at all times.

Rabbits. Eat the young shoots of small trees, and in winter will eat the bark off the stems of the young trees. Exclude by fencing, keep the fences checked regularly for maintenance, and shoot any rabbits which get into the plantations. With exceptionally good trappers, and with co-operation from neighbours, it may be possible in rare cases to plant without fencing.

Hares. Eat the young shoots off trees, and often leave them lying on the ground. It may be necessary, where hares are very numerous in the locality, to heighten fences by an additional wire. Hares must be rigorously controlled by shooting.

Deer, Red, Roe, Fallow, Japanese. These various species of deer damage trees by eating the young shoots in severe weather, rubbing and stripping the bark off the trunk of the tree when they are rubbing the fur off their newly grown antlers. They should be excluded by specially high fences where the population of deer warrant this, or be well controlled by shooting where there are only a few in the district.

Red Squirrel. Apart from storing and feeding on hardwood tree seed, the red squirrel chews the cones of many of our common trees. It also eats the bark off tree stems where the bark is thin, and may completely girdle the tree, and so kill off the top of the tree. these should be controlled to reasonable numbers by shooting.

Grey Squirrel. This animal has recently very rapidly spread over a great part of England, and Wales, while it is also found in central Scotland. Apart from eating the seeds, cones and berries off trees, this animal feeds on buds and young shoots of most kinds of forest trees. But one damage caused by this animal which is of considerable economic importance to the woodland owner, is the fact that the grey squirrels strip the bark off the stems of trees, about mid summer, preferring broadleaved trees from twenty to forty years old. Sycamore especially suffers, but Beech is also very liable to be attacked. Grey squirrels should be completely exterminated on every estate, and the best method is by shooting. Dreys should be poked at from below by specially made light poles, whilst a keeper stands by to shoot at any squirrels disturbed. This is best done in winter and early spring before the trees flush into leaf. All dreys should be attacked systematically, and destroyed. Any fresh invasion can be readily detected. Special cage trapping can also be very effective if the traps are set at points regularly frequented by grey squirrels, while spring traps may be used, provided they are set in artificial tunnels.

Voles. Periodically these small animals become a temporary plague in certain localities. They eat the bark off the stem of young trees near ground level and will completely ring trees and so kill them. There is little that the forester can do against these animals, as it is not worth endeavouring to trap them. Fortunately as soon as they increase, their natural enemies (owls, hawks and weasels) invade the locality and kill them off.

Fire. The damage and loss from fire can be very high in young plantations and the work and expense of many years may go up in smoke in a few hours. Everything must be done to minimise the risk of a forest fire, and all preparation must be made to tackle any outbreak of fire as quickly as possible. A few men quickly on the scene of a fire, with the right equipment, and properly trained in the use of that equipment, can often save far more than a host of men ill equipped and ill trained arriving after the fire has got full hold. Therefore in the danger periods from February to October, everyone in forestry must be on the alert. The spring months until the end of May when the new vegetation has appeared are especially dangerous, and young conifer woods where there is a lot of molinia grass, and in hardwood areas where there is bracken and gorse are especially vulnerable.

Fires are caused by careless smokers throwing away matches, cigarette ends and tapping out pipes, by careless picknickers leaving fires not properly extinguished, by railway engines throwing out sparks and dropping cinders, by moor, heath, gorse or grass burning getting beyond control or not properly extinguished.

The risk of fire entering or damaging a plantation can be minimised by certain protective measures. These include:— Planting mixtures of conifers and broadleaved trees; by breaking up the woods by properly sited and maintained fire traces (strips of land kept free of all vegetation, or where the vegetation is kept very low by cutting by scythe and removing); by planting fire breaks of Japanese Larch trees at close spacing, say 3 feet by 3 feet. The Japanese Larch is fast growing and soon kills off all vegetation in a few years. The Japanese Larch trees do not burn very quickly and thus make an ideal fire-break. Trees along roadsides may be brashed early, and the brashing carried into the wood, so reducing the risk of fire.

Plan of Action against Fire. A very short plan of action to be taken to prevent fires and to fight fires if they do start, should be drawn up and revised each year. The forester and all the workers should know the contents of the plan,

and the action which they should take in case of outbreak
of fire. This plan should assess the risk of fire at the various
parts of the forest, and should specify:—

Fire Brooms or Beaters. The numbers to be prepared
and where to be sited at suitable centres with a considerable
reserve at a convenient depot. Various types of fire brooms
are in use, the most common types being:—Birch or Ash
handle with head of birch twigs carefully prepared and
wired on, head of old sacks (suitable for grass fires where
there is a good supply of water for wetting), head of old
leather belting about six to seven inches wide, head of old
oil drum lids (suitable for fires in heather).

Water Supplies. It may be possible to build small dams
on ditches or streams in the forest at accessible points. The
dams must be inspected regularly and cleaned of any
silting. Small portable canvas dams may be held in readiness
at a depot, where they can be filled and kept filled during
fire danger periods.

Other Equipment. Axes, saws, spades, mattocks,
knapsack sprayers, old sacks, portable power water pumps
with hoses, should all be listed and a note made as to where
this equipment is stored, and how access can be got to it.
This equipment should be checked over regularly, especially the mechanical equipment.

Patrols. The plan should list where it may be necessary
to have men patrolling roads, railways, etc., and define
their duties and method of dealing with and reporting
fires. On large areas, especially near tourist centres, it may
be necessary to erect fire look-out towers, where a large
area of the forest and surrounding country can be seen.
These towers to be manned in danger periods, and the
towers to be linked by private field or public telephone to
the forester's house. Maps should be provided in the tower
and instruments, to record the compass bearings of fires,
installed for greater accuracy in reporting outbreaks.

Sources of Labour. The plan should state what local
forest labour is available, and arrangements should be made

with neighbours and other local supplies of labour for assistance in time of need. Contact should always be made, and renewed annually with the Chief Officer or Firemaster of the local fire brigade, while similar arrangements can often usefully be made with local establishments of the armed services.

Alarms. A definite fire alarm system should be devised and defined, ensuring that it does not conflict with any existing local noises or arrangements. This alarm should be clearly understood by all workers.

Telephones. A list of telephone numbers of all people promising assistance should be kept by the forester on a card by his telephone. This would list local police, fire brigade, neighbours, and possibly local service establishments. Many precious minutes may be saved by having these telephone numbers readily available.

Fire Fighting. Conditions vary with species, age of forest, topography, etc., so that no hard and fast rules for fire fighting can be laid down. All forest staff should be trained to tackle fires in grass and young woodlands along the sides, trying to bring the fire to a point. This may be done by hand beating, or hand beating combined with water spraying. It should be emphasised that much energy may be conserved by not raising fire beaters too high in the air. In fact it is highly dangerous to raise beaters too high as sparks and burning debris may be thrown over the head of the fire fighter thus starting other fires behind his back. In older woods it may be necessary to go ahead of the fire and cut out trees to make a fire break, or even to start a counter fire, although the latter is exceptional and must only be done by experienced men. The purpose of this is to remove the fuel for the fire and thus cause the fire to burn itself out. If the fire is large the man in charge may not be fighting the fire himself, but organising the fire fighters, arranging the reliefs, refreshments, etc.

After the fire has been got under control, it is essential to keep men on guard duty going round all smouldering parts, damping down with water, and ensuring that there is no possible risk of a further outbreak. Check over all equipment and arrange for replacements immediately to ensure that all preparations are ready in case of another outbreak.

Insects. Thousands of species of insects live in woodlands or in land suitable for afforestation, but no insect wholly precludes the planting of trees. The presence of certain insects, such as the Pine Weevil, may delay the replanting of felled conifer woodlands by a conifer species. Considerable damage or reduction of vigour may result from the presence of insects. There is very little practical action that a forester may take against insects, apart from planting mixtures (especially broadleaved species with conifers), by keeping plantations healthy at all times, and even by encouraging insectivorous birds to live and nest in the forest by providing nesting boxes.

Insects undergo a metamorphosis during their life, and generally that metamorphosis includes three stages and is called Complete Metamorphosis. These three stages are:— The egg, from which hatches the larva, which feeds and pupates in a cocoon. From the pupal cocoon emerges the adult insect. If any of these stages are missed out, and this happens with several families of insects, the larval stage is omitted, and by Incomplete Metamorphosis the adult insect appears.

Insects may do damage in the larval and adult stages. The type of damage done by these insects to forest trees may be divided into the following various groups. The life histories and damage and control of these insects cannot be dealt with in detail in such a book as this, but there are one or two good books on Forest Entomology, and the Forestry Commission publish excellent descriptive leaflets on the major forest insect pests.

Borers in Seed, Acorns, etc. This group includes the Seed Fly which in the larval stage feeds on the seed of

Douglas Fir and Silver Fir, and also the Nut Weevil which feeds on acorns. In practice, there is nothing which the forester can do to reduce or prevent damage by these insects.

Root Feeders. In this group the damage is mainly done in the larval stage of the insects. Much damage can be done in nurseries by Chafer Beetle larvae, by Cutworms, and by Wireworms (larvae of Click Beetles). The forester can reduce the numbers of Chafer larvae by deep digging or cultivation and hand picking the white larvae, and by the use of soil fumigants. Poison bait, including Paris Green on Bran, may be laid on the ground for Cutworms. Care must be exercised in handling Paris Green. Rhubarb sticks just buried underground about two inches have proved very effective in attracting wireworms, and the wireworms can then be hand picked and destroyed. This should be done daily. The rhubarb should be renewed weekly.

Bark Feeders. The larvae of many insects breed and feed under the bark of trees, adult insects also feed on the outer bark of the stem and roots of trees. Included in this group are:—Pine Shoot Beetle, Pine Weevil, Ash Bark Beetle, Spruce Bark Beetle, and various species of sucking insects on Larches, Silver Fir, Weymouth Pine and Beech. The forester should reduce to a minimum the breeding ground and food for these insects by the removal of suppressed, dying and dead trees. Where thinnings have been made in conifer woods, particularly Pines, the timber should be removed as soon as possible or have the bark peeled off. If the bark dries out quickly there is little feeding for the insects. Traps, consisting of thin-barked Pine billets, about two feet long with sprays of fresh Pine twigs laid over them and partially buried by turf, are effective against adult Pine Weevils. The traps should be examined regularly and the weevils handpicked. The material of the traps should be renewed as required.

Borers in Buds, Leaves, Shoots. This boring may be

done during the larval or adult stage. Included in this group are the Ash Bud Moth, Larch Shoot Borer, Pine Shoot Beetle and Pine Shoot Moth. Again there is very little that the forester can do to prevent the ravages of these insects. If the leading bud of an Ash tree is attacked the tree will fork and will require to be pruned if this forking is in the first twenty feet. The shoots of Larches may be killed off, and the same happens in the case of Pine, but with Pines, after strong winds, short pieces of shoot will litter the ground, and these shoots will be found to be hollow due to boring by the beetle larvae. Very seldom is the leading shoot attacked and the crowns generally show a stunted growth of side shoots where the beetles are very numerous. The Pine Shoot Beetle breeds under the thin bark of suppressed conifers. Peel all felled timber, bark exposed stumps. Larch Shoot Moth larvae feed in shoot and may kill off shoots. No artificial method of control. The larvae of the Pine Shoot Moth feed in the buds of the shoots of Scots Pine mainly and Corsican Pine. Often feed in the growing buds and cause severe distortion of the shoot; often the leading shoot is attacked. Less damage in mixed woods, otherwise little artificial control action which the forester can take.

Leaf Feeders and Defoliators. This group includes several species of aphids on Spruces and Silver Firs—Larch Leaf Miner, Winter Moth and Mottled Umber Moth, Oak Leaf Roller Moth, Pine Sawfly and Pine Looper Moth. The aphids mainly suck from the leaves of conifers and reduce the vigour of the tree, sometimes killing off the needles and causing severe check to growth. No action can be taken by the forester. The caterpillar of the Larch Leaf Miner feeds on the leaves in July, mostly on younger trees, and may cause considerable defoliation. No artificial method of control is advocated. The larvae of the Winter Moth, Mottled Umber Moth and the Green Oak Roller Moth all feed on the young foliage of Oak, and in seasons can cause severe defoliation by early summer and thus severe check to growth. Birds such as starlings, tits and finches feed on these larvae, otherwise no artificial control has been devised although dusting from aeroplanes has been carried out on the Continent. The caterpillars of the Pine Sawfly feed on the previous year's needles from May to July, and may cause severe defoliation. In epidemic years clusters of larvae may be squashed by forest workers with glove-protected hands. The Pine Looper Moth larvae feed on the needles of Scots and Corsican Pine and can cause serious defoliation. An outbreak of epidemic proportions occurred in 1953 and this may lead to further serious outbreaks. The damage occurs mainly to plantations in the pole stage and any Autumn browning of foliage should be investigated.

Gall Formers on Buds, Shoots and Foliage. Though this group does not cause any serious damage, activities of these insects may reduce the vigour of the crop and reduction of quality of crop. Included in the group are various aphids on Pines, Spruces and Silver Fir—the Pine Resin-gall Moth, Oak Apple Gall formers etc. Of minor importance to the forester, there is no artificial action which the forester can take against the insects of this group.

Wood Borers. This group may be sub-divided into two sections, (a) Those boring in growing trees and (b) those boring in stored timber, furniture etc. The larvae again do most of the damage and in section (a) we find such insects as Goat Moth, Leopard Moth, Pin-hole Borers and Wood Wasp larvae doing most damage. Apart from keeping the woods healthy and clean there is no artificial action the forester can take against these beetles. Included in the second section are the Furniture Beetles, Powder Post Beetles, Stag Beetles, etc. A considerable loss occurs every year from the ravages of these beetles, but the protection of the timber from damage by insects is outside the scope of this book. Several chemical solutions are available for treatment of timber to reduce the damage done by these insects.

Fungi. There are again many fungi, both parasitic and saprophytic, in British woodlands, but only one, a rust has precluded planting of a tree species, Weymouth Pine. Another leaf fungus on Western Red Cedar has restricted its use as a forest tree in this country. There is little practical action which the forester can take against fungi. Fungi may be considered under the following classes.

Nursery Diseases. These are fungi mainly causing leaf cast (as with Larch) and damping off of seedlings. Use Cheshunt Compound spray, or Potassium permanganate as a spray.

Root Diseases. Mainly rots, such as Honey Fungus and Conifer Heart Rot. Restrict choice of species when planting on sites liable to these rots. Considerable heart rot may be expected where there are fluctuations in the water table.

Leaf Diseases. Mainly on Sycamore, Western Red Cedar, Douglas Fir and Pines. Keep plantations healthy and vigorous. Remove sickly trees at the earliest opportunity. Leaf spot on Sycamore is not serious.

Rusts. These fungi usually have two hosts, one being often a Pine and the other host a garden weed or plant. The spread of these fungi is therefore difficult to control. Apart from the rust attacking and often killing Weymouth Pine, others are not so serious. There is little that a forester can do to control the damage done by these fungi.

Stem Diseases. These occur on European Larch, Douglas Fir and other conifers, and cause cankers on Poplars and wilt on Elms. Plant resistant Poplar species. Keep conifer plantations healthy and damage will be lessened. The stem disease, causing wilt, on Elm is fairly serious in England, but so far has not reached far into Scotland.

Diseases on Timber. Timber, after having been sawn and stacked, often becomes streaked blue. This is a fungus which spoils the colour and appearance of the timber, but does not reduce the strength of the timber. Dry Rot is a very serious problem in buildings where unseasoned and untreated timbers have been used and where moist air collects. Always use seasoned and preserved timbers in buildings.

Many of these fungi are described in detail in the series of leaflets published by the Forestry Commission.

CHAPTER XII

FELLING, EXTRACTION, CONVERSION, PRESERVATION AND UTILISATION OF PRODUCE

An owner of woodlands may have marked some thinnings or clear fellings, and may decide to sell the timber standing, to fell it by his own labour and sell at the stump, or to fell, extract and convert into products by his own labour, and then sell the produce. The owner will first consider the economics of the operation, and whether it will pay him to lay out capital on equipment. This will mainly depend on whether there is to be a regular annual felling of sufficient quantities to justify the outlay. If, however, the owner decides to sell standing, he will clearly mark all trees which are to be included in the transaction, and the sale will be covered by a proper legal sales agreement which should include clauses to cover the following points:—

1. Reference to name of estate, parish, county etc., and attached map with area coloured green for clear fellings and coloured red for thinnings. The map to be signed by both parties.

2. Statement of number of trees and volume, and how they can be identified. This to be supported by a clause that purchaser must have satisfied himself as to count and contents of trees.

3. Clause stating the purchase price, method of payment and date of entry. Date of clearance to be fixed, and penalty for failure to clear within specified time.

4. The timber sold to be at the risk of the purchaser from a fixed time and date.

5. Define all reservations, such as trees banded with white paint etc.

6. Agreement on sites for plant, sawmills, huts for employees of purchaser, slab and sawdust heaps and timber stacking sites. Final date for removal of equipment and restoration of site, and penalty for failure to comply with this clause.

7. If owner of timber also holds rights for water supplies on the area, a clause should be inserted giving purchaser of timber rights to water supplies after local commitments have been met.

8. Clause binding purchaser to take precautions against damage to roads, drains, bridges, fences, walls, etc., and any damage thereto to be made good at purchaser's expense. A report on the condition of all these features before timber operations begin, to be prepared, and to form part of the agreement and to be signed by both parties.

9. Define the roads and accesses, which purchaser may use, and if necessary type of vehicle which may be used, rubber wheeled, etc.

10. A clause ensuring that the purchaser takes full responsibility for any damage due to fires arising from his operations.

11. Any trees felled, but not in the original contract, to be paid for at valuation.

12. Statement as to disposal of lop and top in clear felling. Seller may reserve the tops of Norway Spruce near Christmas to sell as Christmas trees, and he may also reserve the right to collect cones from the trees being felled. The purchaser may be required to pile and burn all lop and top, within specified dates if near other plantations. To include a penalty clause if necessary, for failure to clear ground as required.

13. Any trees damaged by the operations, if dealing with thinning, to be left standing, but penalty of so much per tree so damaged to be paid by purchaser.

14. A clause binding the conditions of sale and allowing for the appointment of a referee in case of dispute.

Appendices. Maps and Report on the condition of roads, walls, fences, bridges, etc.

Sales of felled produce at the stump. The contract will be on similar terms as for a standing sale, except that the measurements may be made mutually, and merely a price per cubic foot per species laid down in the sale agreement.

Long Term Sales. It may be more attractive to prospective purchasers to know that they can buy regular annual amounts, and it may therefore be advantageous to both parties to arrange a long term sale for thinnings and clear fellings. In such cases it would be necessary to have a clause inserted to enable prices to be varied by either side according to market prices, and a clause enabling the seller to terminate the contract on default of the purchaser.

Equipment for Felling. For coppice cuttings a form of heavy billhook is best. For early thinnings a light axe is best, but many workers do not like a light axe. When thinnings become a bit heavier, a "Bushman" type saw is usually preferred, although much depends on local custom. By the time trees are over about nine inches in diameter the best tool is a double handled crosscut saw with raker teeth. Power saws are as yet not very portable, but are useful for large diameter trees and especially for cross-cutting large trees. Wedges and cant hooks or "peevies" are an essential part of tree fellers equipment. In all cases sharpness and care of tools must be stressed, as this will lead to more efficient working.

Tree Felling. If possible all trees should be felled in the same direction, more especially in thinnings, as this usually helps the extraction of the trees from the wood. Trees should not be felled across ridges and ravines, to save snapping, and also to assist with the extraction of the trees. The spurs where the strong side roots develop should be trimmed so that the stem of the tree is extended cylindrically downwards to nearly ground level. This is done by axe, and a small face is cut into the stem on the side on which the tree is to fall in order to give it space and leverage to fall. This operation is called "laying-in," and should not be overdone, but should be sufficient to prevent the tearing of the bole of the tree when it is falling.

Extraction. If the owner of timber decides that he is to do the felling by his own labour force, then he has to consider whether to do the extraction of the felled produce by his own labour. If there is to be a fairly large annual quantity of produce coming out of the woods, then it may justify capital expenditure on suitable equipment. If there is only small irregular amounts to come out, the owner may decide to sell at stump, or engage a contractor who has the skill and equipment to do the work for him at a fixed contract rate. If an owner decides to extract himself, he has first to decide whether any crosscutting of the trees should be done before extraction. As far as possible trees should be extracted in full length, but after the third thinning the trees may be too heavy and some crosscutting is often necessary. The owner will decide on the method of extraction. This depends on the quantity to be removed and on the terrain over which the produce is to be extracted, whether steep or flat, even or uneven, soft or hard, etc.

It is in the extraction of produce that much money can be saved or wasted. Every time a tree or pole is handled from stump to sawbench, adds pence to its cost of production. Therefore reduce the number of handlings to a minimum. One other point in saving labour or effort is that once the timber is off the ground on to a wagon, then do not let it be thrown off on to the ground again, as this means that the workers have to use up a considerable amount of energy in lifting the log. Always build ramps so that once the produce is up at working level, it can be kept at working level. Use mechanical means for loading where possible, a "Hiab Hoist" on a lorry will reduce manual effort tremendously. Where the trees are being extracted in thinnings, always protect the base of the standing trees on the sides of extraction lanes by driving in stakes against the butts.

Possible Methods of Extraction. These can be sub-divided into, (a) Man, (b) Horse, (c) Power, (d) Gravity.

Man. Man can generally carry produce up to one cubic foot in volume a distance of about twenty yards economically for a day. Anything heavier than this should not be carried by man. In first and possibly second thinnings the produce could be carried into lanes at about two chain intervals, and from these lanes can be extracted by horse. On steep slopes a man can lift the butts of trees off the ground by short rope or wire slings and slide the trees down the hill. Again this is not a very safe method and applies only to light produce in the long length.

Horse. This is still one of the most economic methods of extraction, especially for thinnings. Useful for hauls up to about 300 yards. Often the timber is dragged on the ground, simply bound in a drag chain attached to the swingletree. The pull by the horse keeps the chain taut round the load. Often the poles are pulled point first as they are slightly flexible, and lift slightly off the ground, and are more likely to glide over obstacles such as stones and tree stumps. If pulled butt end first, the butts are heavy and do not lift and are therefore inclined to be knocked out of the chain when they hit an obstacle, in spite of any butt swellings. When pulled along the ground the timber has much soil embedded in the bark, and this will spoil saws when crosscutting or splitting. Also the dragging of the timber along the ground will make hollows in the ground, which, in high rainfall, will become drains and water will pour down the hillside. For these reasons, several types of attachment have been developed for pulling loads by horse. These may be "slipes" or sledge, sulkey, and pole wagon. A slipe consists of two short runners, about ten inches deep made from three inch thick timber, with a cross-spar or bolster rigidly connecting the runners, making the whole outfit about three feet long by three feet wide. The butts of logs or poles are piled on the bolster. A chain is fixed to an iron ring on the underside of the bolster, passes over the load, through the iron ring on to the swingletree. Again the pull by the horse keeps the chain taut and prevents the load from slipping. This method is used on soft uneven ground for long thinnings. The sulkey is two wheeled rubber tyred, with a swivel bolster built up on the axle, about three feet wide. Butts of poles are piled on this bolster, and chained round, and the pull is again on this chain, keeping the load in position. It is used on soft, but fairly even ground, and it has the advantage that it can be used between the rows of trees for the extraction of thinnings. The four wheeled rubber tyred pole wagon is more used for heavy short logs, and is only suitable where there is room to move and manoeuvre, such as in clear felling, and where the ground is not too steep and uneven.

Power. This can be in the form of rubber tyred tractors, track-laying or crawler tractors, static powered winch or powered cableways. The tractors can be used with powered winches for heavy logs, with chains, sledges, sulkeys or with pole wagons. They are very useful for longer hauls and for heavier timber, but not very easily manoeuvred amongst standing crops in the thinning stage without doing damage to butts of trees left standing. Also track-laying tractors cannot be used on public roads beyond the boundaries of woods or fields, and this means linking up with some other form of transport. Therefore on soft ground, wheeled tractors could have specially large diameter wheels fitted with wide tyres, and the pole wagons could have large diameter wheels also. Narrow gauge track-laying tractors such as are used by airborne forces have been found very useful for the extraction of thinnings. Stationary power winches are not often used, but are very suitable for getting heavy timber out of gullies or ravines. The best form of power winch is that which is mounted on a tractor, and powered by its engine; it will draw a heavier load than the moving tractor can pull. Powered cableways have not been used very much in Britain, although they have been used abroad in such countries as Switzerland. Capital outlay is high. Suitable for steep and uneven country in Wales and West Scotland, where large regular quantities are being extracted. Narrow gauge railways powered by small diesel engines have been used on flatter ground, but are expensive to lay and are not very portable if extraction operations move from one part of the forest to another in rotation.

Gravity. This can only be used on steep hillsides where large quantities of timber are to be extracted. Some form of chute made from timber, iron or aluminium alloy is laid on the ground across slopes at gradients of about 25 degrees. The section of the chute is about eighteen inches deep, and about eighteen inches wide at the top. Water may have to be poured down the chute before timber is slid down, but in wet, snowy, or frosty weather timber will speed down the chute, and on bends may be inclined to jump, therefore full safety precautions must be taken. Cableways supported at intervals down the hill have been used. In one pattern the descent of the loaded carriages, controlled by brake, pulls the empty carriage up on a parallel cable. In another, simpler form, one cable is used for both descending and ascending carriages, alternately.

Roads. If tracks or cheaply constructed roads can be made through the forest, this will speed up extraction, and may reduce the number of times the timber has to be handled and so reduce extraction costs. All that may be necessary is to put gravel or stone in the tracks where the wheels will run. Always ensure that good efficient drains are made on either side of the road, and that the water from those drains has a suitable outlet.

Conversion of Produce. It is not proposed to deal with sawmilling as it is more a mechanically technical subject. The small woodland owner will either sell his timber standing, or felled at stump, or at roadside, either prepared or unprepared. With pitwood, however, an owner may decide to prepare props by his own forest labour. The pitwood poles, having been brought into a central depot or depots, should be piled on ramps. It should then be peeled (have the bark removed). This may be done by hand, using special peeling spades or draw knives. Where larger scale operations are taking place it may justify the outlay to instal a power peeler. After peeling, the timber will pass on to another ramp, from which it will be crosscut. Although pitwood may be crosscut into pitprops by hand with a bow saw, many small estates will have saws powered off tractors which are quite suitable for this propping. If not, there are two types of portable saw benches on the market for propping. One has small iron wheels with a fixed bench, and the other has rubber tyred wheels with a moveable bench. One runs on petrol, the other on diesel. It is essential that the saws be kept in very good trim, and that all safety precautions, as required by the Factories Acts, are taken.

If sales, or prospective sales, allow, try to cut at least two different diameters for the same length of prop. As has been mentioned earlier, pitprops are sold by length and minimum top diameter under bark. Therefore, for any length, say three feet, the sawyers should be given three inches, and three and a half inches top diameters to cut. This speeds up cutting as the sawyers mainly concentrate on cutting to length, and the man stacking can sort out the different diameters. There are many sizes of props required by the mines, but the number of sizes to be cut on one estate should be restricted to a few, as it would take a long time to cut wagon loads of all sizes. It has been found from experiment for strength of props that the diameter is the same in inches as the length is in feet. That is, we get 3 feet props with 3 inch top diameter in demand, and $3\frac{1}{2}$ feet with $3\frac{1}{2}$ inches top diameter, 4 feet with 4 inches top diameter and so on. After cutting, the props are stacked in rows running in alternate directions, i.e. with alternate rows at right angles to each other, criss-cross fashion, and it is useful for counting purposes to have ten, twelve or fifteen props in each row. This method of stacking allows the air to move freely through the stack and so season the timber. Stacks should be kept off the ground, and all weed growth cut from round the piles to prevent an accumulation of moist air. Prepared props may be sold through timber merchants or direct to consumers.

Preservation of Timber. By treating timber with some form of preservative, its useful life may be extended many years. Some timbers which would last only a few years, for example, in contact with ground, will by preservation, especially under pressure, last from fifteen to twenty years. This applies particularly to species of Pine, Spruces, Douglas Fir, and even to Birch. Only a few timbers, such as Oak, Sweet Chestnut, Larch, Cedar and Yew are naturally durable, and even with these the durability is confined to the heartwood, the sapwood being perishable.

Most timbers even when untreated will last a long time if kept permanently dry or always wet; but a great deal of timber has to be used in alternately wet and dry conditions, especially out of doors, and under such circumstances decay can be very rapid. The main causes of decay of timber are of purely organic origin, and arise from attacks by fungi or insects. If timber can be made unfit for food for insects or fungi, then its life will be preserved for many years. Even seasoning, with the resultant loss of moisture content can act as a form of preservation. Timber can therefore be preserved so as to increase its durability in one or other of the following six different methods.

1. Seasoning naturally in the open air.
2. Drying artificially by heated air.
3. Dissolving the sap.
4. Steaming.
5. Superficial application of preservatives.
6. Impregnation with antiseptics.

The oldest of all such processes, and still very suitable, is that of charring the surface of the wood before it is put into the ground.

Seasoning Naturally in the open air. This can be

carried out in all woodlands. The timber is piled off the ground, and so that there is free movement of air through the pile. With thin sawn timber, separating pieces called "stickers" must be inserted across the length of the pile at regular intervals, and must be directly above one another in the pile. Some form of roof to carry off rain may be built over stacks of sawn timber. Some months of seasoning in the piles will reduce the moisture content so that the timber will last longer in use. But air seasoning will not produce timber suitable for indoor work in centrally heated buildings. In order to reduce the moisture content to a level suitable for house building purposes, it must be dried artificially. Seasoning makes timber much lighter, somewhat harder and stronger, and much less liable to change its shape.

Drying Artificially by Heated Air. This is not generally done on woodland estates, as the outlay on equipment is not justified unless there is a large regular quantity to be treated. This process is called Kiln Seasoning and is carried out in large brick kilns. The moisture content of the timber to be seasoned is calculated before the timber is piled into the kiln. Hot moist air is first forced in, so that the timber will not be dried too quickly on the surface. The moisture in the timber is converted by the heat into steam and by controlling the temperature and moisture content of the air within the kiln for several days, the actual moisture content of the timber can be reduced to about 12 per cent, which is a suitably low concentration for use in most building operations.

Dissolving the Sap. The simplest way of dissolving the sap is to immerse logs for a long time in running water, in a stream or canal. This is a very slow and gradual process, as the sap can only be washed out by diffusion. By removing the sap and replacing it with water the food of some fungi is removed and the timber is made more durable. The timber must then be air seasoned.

Steaming. This is used for sawn timber only. The

F

timber is enclosed in special wooden chambers, into which steam can be fed. When steaming is in progress the condensed water is run off. This is clear at first; then becomes darker in colour and has a woody smell. Steaming is continued until the water runs clear again. This takes from 40 to 80 hours and the resultant timber is usually slightly darker than the original. The steamed wood is lighter and less likely to warp and split than unsteamed wood. Whilst warm and moist, it is very flexible and in cooling and drying it retains the form given to it while still warm and moist. This quality is made use of in bending wood for several uses including furniture making.

Superficial Application of Preservatives. This can be done in two different ways.

Polishing with wax, etc., is for the direct purpose of improving the appearance of the wood, although it indirectly also preserves it by hermetically closing the superficial pores.

Painting or coating superficially with oil paint, oil, coal tar, wood tar, and tar products, also linseed oil and varnish close the superficial pores of the wood and therefore prevents warping and splitting due to hygroscopic changes and hinders the entrance of fungal spores. But if the wood be painted while still green, the effect is only to make it rot quicker by preventing the evaporation of the moisture still contained in excess of what there should be in an air dried condition.

Impregnation with Antiseptics. The first essential for fungal and insect life is an available supply of ready made food. Preservation consists of the poisoning of this food by application of some toxic liquid to the wood. The cellular structure of the wood greatly facilitates this process as most cells communicate with their neighbours by means of pits, through which the preservative can pass. This explains why sapwood in which the pits are open is usually more easily impregnated than heartwood, where many of the pits are closed.

No ideal preserving fluid has been found to satisfy all the requirements of a complete preservative. It should be toxic to all fungi and insects, but non-poisonous to human beings and animals. It should penetrate deeply and easily into the wood and remain there and not be liable to be washed out. It should be cheap and easily obtainable in large quantities, colourless and odourless. It should be non-corrosive in contact with metals.

There are three main types of preservative in general use, the oily—such as creosote, the water soluble—such as Sodium Fluoride, Zinc Chloride, Mercuric Chloride, and the solvent type which is mostly used in the proprietory preservatives.

Creosote and Creosoting. Creosote is an oil derived from the distillation of coal or wood during the preparation of tar. A simple method for creosoting small quantities of timber for fencing, etc., is as follows. Make a small brick fireplace and place over this an empty drum from which one end has been removed. Have the fence stakes peeled and air dried. Stack them in with their points downwards and add creosote until about two feet deep. Light a fire underneath and heat until the temperature is about 200 degrees Fahrenheit, and keep at that temperature for an hour. Allow to cool for at least twelve hours, as it is during the cooling that the creosote enters the wood. The heating only causes the air and water in the wood to expand and come out of the wood, and their place is taken by the creosote. Some timbers absorb more creosote than others. Those easy to creosote include:—Alder, Ash, Beech, Birch, Elm, Lime Hornbeam, Poplar, Sweet Chestnut, Willow, Pines and Silver Fir. Those difficult to creosote, if it was desired or necessary to creosote them, include:—Douglas Fir, Larches, Norway Spruce, Cypress, Sitka Spruce, Oak, Thuya and Wellingtonia.

Special creosoting tanks with reserve underground tanks can be purchased for large scale operations. In this case, if after allowing absorption by cooling, the charge is reheated much of the creosote filling the cells will be driven out and saved, but the cell walls will still be covered with preservative. This gives preservation at a reduced cost.

Many types of preservative are on the market, and each type can be used with timber for special purposes, but it is customary to send timber to be preserved rather than to do it on the estate, except for creosoting.

Utilisation of Produce. Certain timbers because of special inherent qualities are used for special purposes, but apart from these which are mentioned later, the following industries are the main users of timber or processed timber.

Conifers. The produce from first and second thinnings are often treated with preservative and used for agricultural and horticultural purposes, such as fencing. Larch is used for rustic work. Where the timber is over three inches in diameter it is used for pitprops. An outlet for this produce which is so far only on a small scale, but is likely to develop is the manufacture of chip board, fibre board (except Larch) or insulation board, and wood pulp for paper. If quantities produced are large enough to make it an economic proposition to set up special processing mills, it is quite possible that those industries will use up very large quantities of this smaller type of produce.

The produce from third and fourth thinnings is generally used for round pitprops, telegraph and electricity transmission poles, for sawing into mining timbers, boxwood logs for sawing into timbers for boxes and crates, packaging, etc. Timber for Rayon industry, and some timber for paper pulp.

The heavier timber from later thinnings and clear fellings may provide some heavier telegraph and transmission poles (Scots Pine and European Larch), sawn timber for housing, railway wagons and railway sleepers, shipbuilding and general industry.

Hardwoods. The demand for pitprops from hardwoods does not amount to any great quantity, and in fact there is no large outlet for early thinnings from hardwoods. In

certain localities small produce can be disposed of for horticultural and agricultural purposes, and much more could be
used after preservative treatment. The turnery and charcoal
industries absorb a certain amount of small hardwood
produce, but it is not likely that those industries will
increase their demands.

The main consumers of sawn hardwood timber are:—
general industry, car, bus and railway coach construction,
domestic furniture, housing, shipbuilding, and food
packing. Future outlets for quality hardwood timber may
develop along the same lines as conifers in that the demand
for processed timber will increase as the supplies justify the
establishment of expensive factories for timber processing.

CHAPTER XIII

SURVEYING

It is essential that records of work proposed and completed should be kept accurately. To support these records one must have good maps of the estate, kept fully up to date. While the Ordnance Survey maps show the main outlines and features of a wood or hillside, they have usually to be supplemented by practical field surveying in order to determine the situation and size of particular plantations, whether these be actually existing or proposed. The normal scales of maps used are the Ordnance Survey six inches to one mile and, where available, for small areas, the twenty five inches to one mile. It must be borne in mind that a map is a plan drawn to scale showing the horizontal positions and distances between points.

The normal standard of length measurement is the chain, which is divided into 100 links (Gunter's Chain).

1 mile   = 8 Furlongs = 80 Chains   = 1760 Yards
1 Furlong = 10 Chains = 220 Yards.
1 Chain   = 22 Yards   = 66 Feet.
1 Chain   = 100 Links each of 7.92 Inches.

The normal standard of measurement of area is one acre or fraction of an acre.

1 Acre = 4 Roods = 10 Square Chains = 160 Perches = 4840 Square Yds.
1 Rood = $2\frac{1}{2}$ Square Chains = 40 Perches = 1210 Square Yards.
1 Perch = $30\frac{1}{4}$ Square Yards.
1 Square Chain = 1 Chain × 1 Chain = 22 Yards × 22 Yards = 484 Square Yards = 1/10th of an Acre.
1 Square Mile = 80 × 80 Square Chains = 6400 Square Chains = 640 Acres.

If we have on the map one line which represents a certain line on the ground, we can plot on the map the position of any other line or point on the ground if we know the length of the perpendicular drawn from a fixed point on this line to the object. This perpendicular measurement is called an *offset*.

For Example. On the map is a line A B, and on the ground this is represented by the line a b. At a distance of 2 chains from a, at point c, a perpendicular line can be drawn to the corner of a fence at d, and the length of this perpendicular line is 1½ chains, then we can plot the position of d on the map as follows:–

On the map, measure along the line A B, on the correct scale, the distance of 2 chains, thus fixing point C on the map. At C set off a line perpendicular to the line A B in the direction D. Along this line perpendicular to C measure off to scale a distance of 1½ chains, and thus fix on the map the position D corresponding to point d on the ground, the corner of the fence.

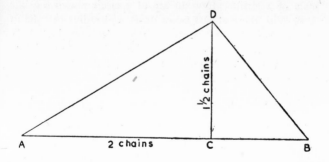

To set off a line perpendicular to the line A B at C proceed as follows. With a compass on point C and any suitable radius draw an arc of a circle to cut the line A B at points M and N. Now with a slightly increased radius on the compass and with the point on M, draw two arcs, one above and one below the line A B. With compass on N and the same radius draw arcs above and below the line A B, and these will cut the arcs drawn from M at points O and P. Then O C P is perpendicular to A B.

If instead of measuring the perpendicular distance from c to d on the ground, the direct distance from a to d is measured and found to be 2 chains, and the direct distance from b to d is $1\frac{1}{2}$ chains.

These lines from a to d and from b to d are called *Tie Lines*. The position of D on the map corresponding to d on the ground is plotted as follows:—

With the compass point on A on the map, and radius to scale of 2 chains, draw an arc of a circle above the line A B. With the compass point on B, and radius to scale of $1\frac{1}{2}$ chains, draw an arc of a circle above the line A B. Where these two arcs intersect will fix the position of D on the map, representing d on the ground.

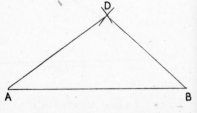

If we have a compass to measure the angle between the lines b a and a d, this will give us the direction of a d, and we must measure the distance of a d on the ground. To plot the position of D on the map to correspond with d on the ground, on the line A B at A set off by protractor the line A X in the direction of a d according to the angle measured on the ground. On this line A X measure off to scale the distance of a d, as measured on the ground, and this will fix D on the map, corresponding to d on the ground.

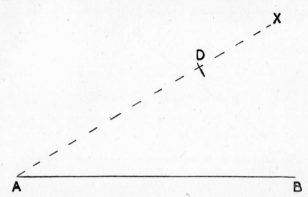

If we have no instrument for measuring the angle between the lines b a and a d on the ground, we can take measurements on the ground by chain to enable us to plot the angle between the two lines. From "a" measure along in the direction of b one chain, arriving at point e. From "a" measure along in the direction of d one chain, arriving at the point f. Measure the distance between e and f by chain. The direction of the line A D on the map can be plotted to represent a d on the ground. With the compass on A on the map and radius of one chain to scale draw an arc of a circle above the line A B, cutting the line A B at E. With the compass on E and radius to scale equal to e f draw another arc of a circle above the line A B, and this will cut the first arc at F. The line A F on the map corresponds to a f on the ground. Continue the line A F the distance of a d to scale, and so fix D on the map, corresponding to d on the ground.

If the angle on the ground between the lines b a and a d had been obtuse instead of acute, then we would proceed as follows. Extend b a one chain to e. Measure up one chain from a in the direction of d arriving at f. Then measure the distance between e and f, also the distance from a d. From these measurements D can be plotted on the map to correspond to d on the ground as follows:—On the map

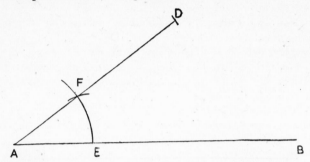

produce the line B A to scale a distance of 1 chain, to point E corresponding to e on the ground. With the compass on A and radius to scale one chain draw an arc of a circle from E upwards. With the compass on point E and radius to scale equal to the measured distance of e f on the ground, draw another arc of a circle. Where these two arcs cut, will fix the point F on the map, corresponding to f on the ground. Measure to scale the distance A D along the line A F according to the distance measured from a to d on the ground.

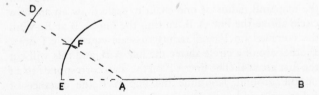

Surveying is the laying out of straight lines on the ground and taking measurement of these lines, and from these lines by means of offsets or tie lines in order to fix positions of other lines or points on the ground which are not yet on the map.

These Field Measurement are recorded in a Field Book.

The instruments used are, Ranging Poles, Gunter's Chain (with ten short wire arrows), Tapes 66 feet or 100 feet (linen or steel), and possibly an optical square.

Ranging Poles. Usually wooden, six feet in length, with metal point at one end. Usually painted red and white or black and white in alternate bands of one foot length.

Gunter's Chain. Steel chain of 100 links, 22 yards, with a brass tally marker at every 10 links. Set of 10 wire arrows accompanies the chain.

Tapes. Usually 66 feet or 100 feet, in either linen or steel. Linen is inclined to stretch, and steel is inclined to twist and may snap if handled carelessly.

Optical Square. A small metal box with two mirrors, and is used to set off right angles from a known position of a line, or to find the point on the line where a perpendicular from an outside object would strike the line of survey.

Reconnaissance and Station Fixing. Before starting a survey, walk thoroughly over the area, if possible with a tracing off the map of the skeleton of the land about to be surveyed. Note any points on the ground which are on the map. Survey stations are fixed on the ground, bearing in mind the following points.

1. Start the survey from a fixed point on the ground which is already on the map.
2. Have as few survey lines as possible.
3. A main chain line (backbone) should, if possible, run through the whole area with triangles built up on it.
4. Use permanent features or fixtures on the ground as stations.
5. Have as few lines as possible with offsets.
6. If offsets or ties are necessary, have them as short as possible. Limit of 100 links.
7. Avoid, as far as possible, obstacles to chainage.
8. If possible, avoid road crossing, mid-road work, and rivercrossings.

Line Ranging. In order that the chainmen may follow a straight line, it is necessary to range the lines with ranging poles.

(a) If the ends of the chain line are visible, place poles at the stations at each end of the line. Range intermediate poles by sighting on the base of the pole at the far station.

(b) If the ends of the chain line are not intervisible, proceed as follows:—Suppose A and B are two stations, and between them is a short sharp hillock. Place ranging poles at A and B. Direct an assistant to take a ranging pole to a point over the brow of the hill, from which he can just see A, siting himself as near as he can judge on the line A–B, and the point where he puts his ranging pole is D_1. Another assistant with a ranging pole climbs up the hill until he can just see the pole at station B. The first assistant lines him in roughly with point A, and this second pole is placed in the ground at C_1. The assistant at C_1 then directs the assistant at D_1 to a point D_2 which is in line with C_1 and B. Then the pole at C_1 is moved to C_2 which is in line with D_2 and A. This process is repeated until no further movement of poles is required, thus a line is ranged from A to B with intermediate stations at C and D. If the brow of the hill is long, it may be necessary to have three men with poles ranging in the line.

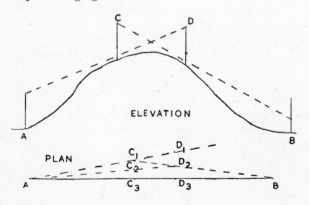

Surveying the Line. Suppose the line A–B has been ranged and is to be chained with a party of three, two chainmen and a surveyor to book. To throw out the chain hold the two handles in the left hand and allow a few links to hang loose, then throw away the chain by the right hand in the direction of chainage. If the chain had been stored properly, it will still be double. The leading chain man takes the arrows and checks that there are ten, takes one end of the chain and pulls in the direction of B. The follower bends down and holds the other end of the chain hard against the base of the pole A. As the leader approaches the chain length he turns to face the follower, with one arrow held against the handle of the chain. He pulls the chain taut and jerks it gently to remove any kinks in it, and is lined in with B by the follower. The leader fixes an arrow at this point, and then pulls forward another chain length, and the same procedure is followed. The follower picks up the arrows until the full length of the line A–B is chained and the arrows are checked with the leader.

If offsets or ties are to be taken from a fixed point on the chain line, the following procedure is adopted. The chain is pulled taut as usual, then laid down on the ground on the chain line. The leader and follower then take the tape, the surveyor lines the leader in at right angles by optical square (or a right angle is set off by the tape first), and the leader pulls out the tape until he reaches the desired point. The follower shouts out the chain distance first followed by the length of the offset, e.g. chain length 5.50, offset left 50 feet, so that the surveyor may enter it in his field book. The same procedure with tie lines except that no right angle is necessary.

The same routine is followed for all the lines of the survey, the angles between the survey lines being measured as described earlier in the introductory paragraphs of this chapter, either by chain or by measuring the angle by compass. To roll up the chain, double it at the centre mark and taking two links at a time, lay them across the palm

of the other hand on a slight angle until the chain is completely rolled up, then tie by the strap, making sure that
the strap passes through the handles to enable the chain
to be carried safely. The arrows are counted and checked.

Booking of Survey Readings. Start from the bottom
of the page and draw two parallel lines close together up
the centre of the page. Start with point A of the line A–B
at the bottom of the page, and in the sample page illustrated
the first booking was at 10 chains from A when a tie to the
corner of a building was taken. This tie was 100 feet in
length. The next entry is the 12 chain mark from which
another tie to the same corner of the same building was
taken. This tie measured 95 feet. From these two readings
the corner of the building is fixed. At the 18 chain mark the
point C of the line C–D joins line A–B on the right hand
side of the survey. On the left hand side of the survey at
every chain length, offsets are taken to the fence round the
plantation. This gives sufficient data for later plotting of
the survey on the map, as the survey started from point A
on the ground which was already on the map.

Errors in Chain Length. Chains should never be used
for a tug-of-war between the leader and the follower.
They should be checked before survey commences against
a length measured by steel tape which is least likely to be
stretched. If a survey has to be made with an incorrect
chain then the true length of chainage can be got from the
following formula.

True Length of Line

$$= \frac{\text{Measured length of line} \times \text{length of incorrect chain}}{\text{Length of True Chain}}$$

To Set Off a Right Angle. Suppose that AB is the chain
line and it is required to set off a right angle at the point C.
This can be done by using the chain or tape as follows.
From point C measure back 40 links or feet towards A.
Get the assistants to hold the end of the chain or tape at C

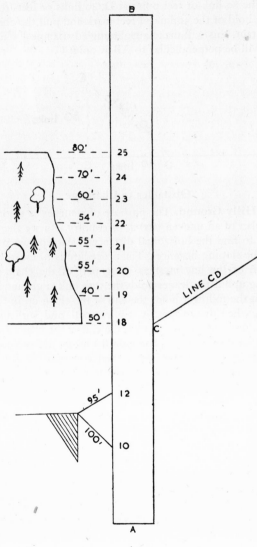

and the 80 link or feet point at D, 40 links or feet from C. Take hold of the 30 link of feet mark and pull the chain or tape taut, this will make a right angled triangle DCE, and CE will be perpendicular to AB at point C.

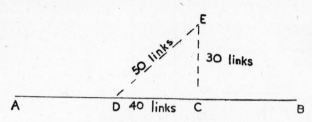

Obstacles to Chainage

1. **Hilly Ground.** The purpose of a survey is to draw a flat plan of an uneven stretch of country and we therefore need to find the horizontal distances between two points, not the sloping distances. The procedure is to measure the length of the line in steps using part of the chain only. Going uphill the leader holds the 50th link at ground level, whilst the follower holds the end of the chain up in the air until, when drawn taut, it is horizontal, and with the aid of a plumb line is able to hold the end of the chain directly over the starting point, and then the leader places an arrow in the ground. The follower then comes up to the 50th link mark whilst the leader goes uphill to hold the other end of the chain. The follower again raises his end of the chain so that it is horizontal and the end plumb above the arrow in the ground. The leader then places the next arrow in the ground. So the line uphill is measured in steps of half a chain, and this must be remembered when checking the arrows at the end of the line. Similar procedure is adopted when chaining downhill.

If there were long even slopes, and we could measure the degree of slope, then we could measure the sloping distance and find the horizontal distance by calculation, from the formula:

Horizontal Distance = Sloping measured distance ×
   Cosine of angle of slope.

For Example. The measured sloping distance is 14
chains and degree of slope is 10 degrees.

   Horizontal Distance = 1400 × Cosine 10, in links.

                  = 1400 × ·9849

                  = 1378·72 links.

Cosines can be found in standard books of mathematical
tables.

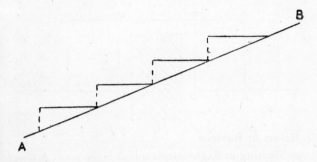

2. Stretch of Water. This may be any object which can
be seen over, but which cannot be chained over, such as a
small loch or pond. Having reached point C on the chain
line, set off a right angle from C to D of known length,
sufficient to pass the obstacle. At D set off DE at right
angles to CD and of known length, sufficient to pass the
obstacle. At E set of EF at right angles to DE and of the
same length as CD. Continue chaining from F. CF = DE
which was measured.

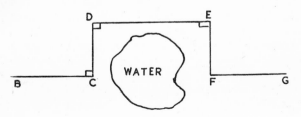

3. Obstacles which cannot be seen over or through.
This may be a dense young wood or a building, and it
would not be possible to range the survey line any further.
At points C and D on the Chain line set off verticals CE and
DF both equal and of known length, sufficient to clear the
obstacle. Range in line EFGH. From G and H set off
verticals GK and HL equal to EC and FD. Then KL is the
continuation of the survey line and DK is equal to FG
which was measured.

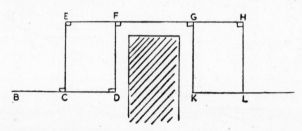

4. Rivers or Ravines

a. Meeting at Right Angles. If A is the point at which
the surveyors have arrived and E a point, stone or tree on
the opposite bank, set off a perpendicular AC of 100 links
with B as mid-point. Set off vertical CD so that D, B and E
are in one straight line. Then measure CD which is equal
to AE and the chainage of E is then determined.

b. Meeting at an angle. Suppose the chain line has to be
continued across the ravine at C. Move along the edge of
the ravine until a point O is reached so that COB is a right
angle. Measure OB and continue the line to X so that
OB = BX. At X draw up a perpendicular XP which
meets the line AB at P. Measure PB and this is equal to
BC. Continue chainage from C.

Angular Measurements by Compass. Prismatic com-
passes are generally used to find the magnetic bearing of a
line, but in order to plot this line we must know the angle
of variation between True North and Magnetic North.
The compass needle is liable to be attracted from its true

reading by any metal causing magnetic attraction. A compass can however be used to find the angle between two lines. Set the compass over the junction of the two lines, take the bearing of first one line and then the other

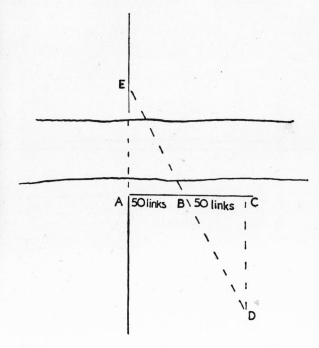

and the difference between the two bearings will give the angle between the two lines, and will be correct irrespective of magnetic attraction.

Plotting the Survey. If the survey has started from a fixed point on the ground, which is also on the map, the survey may be plotted by using the geometrical principles detailed at the start of this chapter. It must be ensured that all lines are measured to the appropriate scale of the map.

Determination of Areas. Having plotted our wood-

lands on the map the next problem is to find the areas of
these woods. This is a comparatively simple matter if the
sides are straight lines. Then it is only a case of breaking
the area up into some of the standard geometrical figures,
if possible rectangles or triangles, whose areas can be
determined.

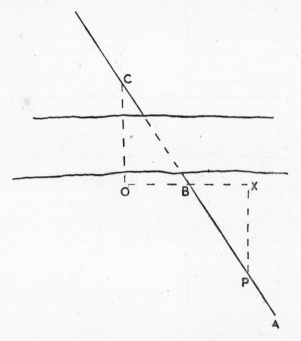

A triangle is a figure bounded by three straight lines, and
the area can be found by multiplying half the length of its
base line, by the length of perpendicular line from the apex
to the base line.

A rectangle is a figure bounded by four straight lines
whose opposite sides are equal and parallel and all its
angles right angles. The area of a rectangle can be found
by multiplying the lengths of two adjacent sides.

A parallelogram is a figure bounded by four straight lines whose opposite sides are equal and parallel, and none of its angles are right angles. Its area can be found by multiplying the length of any one side by the perpendicular distance from the opposite side.

A quadrilateral is a figure bounded by four straight lines. The area of a quadrilateral can be found by dividing it into two triangles and finding the area of these, and adding their areas together.

A rhombus is a quadrilateral which has all its sides equal, but none of its angles are right angles. Its area can be found by drawing a diagonal, so dividing the area into two triangles, whose area can be found.

A trapezium is a quadrilateral which has one pair of parallel sides. The area of a trapezium can be found by multiplying half the sum of the parallel sides by the perpendicular distance between them.

A polygon is a figure bounded by several straight lines, and its area can be found by dividing it up into triangles and finding the sum of their areas.

If a wood is of irregular shape, and has been plotted on the map, then the area can be found by inserting within its boundaries a polygon and finding the area of that polygon. That will leave an irregular strip whose area may be calculated by two methods.

To Find the area of an Irregular strip of ground.

a. Trapezoidal Rule. Divide the area into any number of equal parts by parallel lines closely spaced at equal distances apart, called ordinates. Then the area = half the distance between any two consecutive ordinates × (First ordinate + last ordinate + twice the sum of all the other ordinates).

b. Simpson's Rule. In this case the area is divided up by a series of parallel lines, but it is essential that there should be an odd number of ordinates. The area can then be found from the formula:—Area = One third of the distance between any two consecutive ordinates × (First ordinate + last ordinate + twice the sum of the other odd ordinates + four times the sum of the even ordinates).

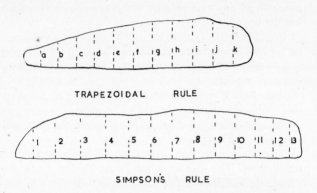

TRAPEZOIDAL   RULE

SIMPSON'S   RULE

Acre Grids. Celluloid acre grids may be purchased at a reasonable price. These are prepared to the scale of six inches to one mile, and are drawn off in rectangles with sides of four chains and two and a half chains, or equal to one acre. They may be divided off into areas of one square chain, equal to one tenth of an acre. If this grid is laid over an area on the map of the same scale, the area in acres of any wood on the map can be easily determined.

Boundaries. Although not truly pertinent to Surveying, it may be appropriate to finish with a definition of some doubtful boundaries. The following usually hold good:—

1. Where there is a hedge without a ditch, or a ditch without a hedge, then the centre of hedge or ditch is the boundary.

2. Where there is a hedge with a ditch on each side, then the centre of the hedge is the boundary.

3. Where there is a hedge with a ditch on one side of it, both hedge and ditch belong to the property more remote from the ditch—that is, the boundary is the edge of the ditch which is furthest from the hedge. The

boundary may be considered to be four feet from the centre of the hedge.

4. Unless a fully mutual fence has been erected, the whole of the fence belongs to the side towards which the nails are driven.

5. In the case of an iron fence, unless it has been erected and maintained mutually, then the boundary is the face of the fence on the side opposite the stays or feet: that is, the fence belongs to the owner of the land on which the stays or feet are set.

Woods Having High Standing Volume per Acre.

Species	Scotland	England	Wales
1. Scots Pine	Novar Estate, Ross-shire.	New Forest, Hampshire.	Tintern, Monmouth.
2. Corsican Pine	Binsness, Morayshire.	Forest of Bere, Hants.	Gwydyr, Caernarvon.
3. European Larch	Murthly, Perthshire.	Haldon, Devon.	Tintern, Monmouth.
4. Japanese Larch	Ardchullary, Perthshire.	Stourton, Wilts.	Leighton, Montgomery.
5. Norway Spruce	Grandtully, Perthshire.	Kielder, Northumberland.	Tintern, Monmouth.
6. Sitka Spruce	Crarae, Argyllshire.	Dunster, Somerset.	Gwydyr, Caernarvon.
7. Douglas Fir	Benmore, Argyllshire.	Tortworth, Gloucester.	Lake Vyrnwy, Mont.

Addendum to Appendix I

	Scotland	England	Wales
1.	4634 H.Ft.O.B. at 52 yrs.	7494 H.Ft.O.B. at 84 yrs.	951 H.Ft.O.B. at 17 yrs.
2.	2249 ,, ,, 45 ,,	6687 ,, ,, 63 ,,	1958 ,, ,, 28 ,,
3.	3037 ,, ,, 48 ,,	3311 ,, ,, 57 ,,	3360 ,, ,, 73 ,,
4.	2810 ,, ,, 47 ,,	3363 ,, ,, 46 ,,	2342 ,, ,, 44 ,,
5.	8502 ,, ,, 46 ,,	4947 ,, ,, 51 ,,	4999 ,, ,, 43 ,,
6.	5343 ,, ,, 66 ,,	5329 ,, ,, 42 ,,	3526 ,, ,, 29 ,,
7.	7324 ,, ,, 66 ,,	9362 ,, ,, 82 ,,	5532 ,, ,, 54 ,,

Number of Trees per Acre

Distance Apart	Number of trees per acre	Distance Apart	Number of trees per acre
3 ft. x 3 ft.	4840	11½ ft. x 11½ ft.	340
3½ ft. x 3½ ft.	3550	12 ft. x 12 ft.	300
4 ft. x 4 ft.	2720	12½ ft. x 12½ ft.	275
4½ ft. x 4½ ft.	2150	13 ft. x 13 ft.	260
5 ft. x 5 ft.	1740	13½ ft. x 13½ ft.	250
5½ ft. x 5½ ft.	1440	14 ft. x 14 ft.	220
6 ft. x 6 ft.	1210	14½ ft. x 14½ ft.	205
6½ ft. x 6½ ft.	1020	15 ft. x 15 ft.	190
7 ft. x 7 ft.	890	15½ ft. x 15½ ft.	180
7½ ft. x 7½ ft.	800	16 ft. x 16 ft.	170
8 ft. x 8 ft.	680	16½ ft. x 16½ ft.	160
8½ ft. x 8½ ft.	600	17 ft. x 17 ft.	150
9 ft. x 9 ft.	540	17½ ft. x 17½ ft.	140
9½ ft. x 9½ ft.	470	18 ft. x 18 ft.	135
10 ft. x 10 ft.	440	19 ft. x 19 ft.	120
10½ ft. x 10½ ft.	410	20 ft. x 20 ft.	110
11 ft. x 11 ft.	370	21 ft. x 21 ft.	100

Areas of Circles for Diameters from 1 inch to 60 inches.

Diam. in Ins.	Area of circle Sq. Ft.	Diam. in Ins.	Area of circle Sq. Ft.	Diam. in Ins.	Area of circle Sq. Ft.	Diam. in Ins.	Area of circle Sq. Ft.	Diam. in Ins.	Area of circle Sq. Ft.
1·0	·0055	10·0	·5454	19·0	1·9689	28·0	4·2761	44·0	10·5592
1·5	·0123	10·5	·6014	19·5	2·0739	28·5	4·4301	45·0	11·0447
2·0	·0218	11·0	·6600	20·0	2·1817	29·0	4·5869	46·0	11·5410
2·5	·0341	11·5	·7214	20·5	2·2922	29·5	4·7464	47·0	12·0482
3·0	·0491	12·0	·7854	21·0	2·4053	30·0	4·9087	48·0	12·5664
3·5	·0669	12·5	·8523	21·5	2·5212	31·0	5·2414	49·0	13·0954
4·0	·0873	13·0	·9218	22·0	2·6398	32·0	5·5851	50·0	13·6354
4·5	·1105	13·5	·9941	22·5	2·7611	33·0	5·9396	51·0	14·1863
5·0	·1364	14·0	1·0690	23·0	2·8852	34·0	6·3050	52·0	14·7480
5·5	·1650	14·5	1·1467	23·5	3·0120	35·0	6·6813	53·0	15·3207
6·0	·1963	15·0	1·2272	24·0	3·1416	36·0	7·0686	54·0	15·9043
6·5	·2304	15·5	1·3104	24·5	3·2748	37·0	7·4667	55·0	16·4988
7·0	·2673	16·0	1·3963	25·0	3·4088	38·0	7·8758	56·0	17·1042
7·5	·3068	16·5	1·4849	25·5	3·5465	39·0	8·2958	57·0	17·7206
8·0	·3491	17·0	1·5763	26·0	3·6870	40·0	8·7266	58·0	18·3478
8·5	·3941	17·5	1·6703	26·5	3·8301	41·0	9·1684	59·0	18·9859
9·0	·4418	18·0	1·7671	27·0	3·9761	42·0	9·6211	60·0	19·6550
9·5	·4923	18·5	1·8666	27·5	4·1248	43·0	10·0847		

Areas of Circles for Circumferences from 3 inches to 96 inches.

Circumference in inches	Area Sq. Ft.	Circumference in inches	Area Sq. Ft.	Circumference in inches	Area Sq. Ft.
3	·0050	34	·6390	65	2·3355
4	·0088	35	·6772	66	2·4079
5	·0138	36	·7160	67	2·4815
6	·0199	37	·7566	68	2·5561
7	·0271	38	·7982	69	2·6318
8	·0354	39	·8408	70	2·7086
9	·0448	40	·8844	71	2·7866
10	·0553	41	·9292	72	2·8641
11	·0669	42	·9571	73	2·9457
12	·0796	43	1·0219	74	3·0264
13	·0934	44	1·0702	75	3·1094
14	·1084	45	1·1184	76	3·1930
15	·1243	46	1·1697	77	3·2774
16	·1415	47	1·2211	78	3·3631
17	·1598	48	1·2733	79	3·4498
18	·1790	49	1·3273	80	3·5376
19	·1996	50	1·3819	81	3·6268
20	·2211	51	1·4378	82	3·7169
21	·2438	52	1·4947	83	3·8082
22	·2675	53	1·5527	84	3·9004
23	·2924	54	1·6121	85	3·9940
24	·3183	55	1·6721	86	4·0877
25	·3455	56	1·7339	87	4·1790
26	·3737	57	1·7970	88	4·2807
27	·4030	58	1·8573	89	4·3786
28	·4335	59	1·9243	90	4·4737
29	·4643	60	1·9883	91	4·5776
30	·4971	61	2·0561	92	4·6788
31	·5311	62	2·1244	93	4·7799
32	·5660	63	2·1940	94	4·8844
33	·6020	64	2·2641	95	4·9891
				96	5·0931

Sectional Area Table

¼ Girth inches	Area Sq. Ft.	¼ Girth inches	Area Sq. Ft.	¼ Girth inches	Area Sq. Ft.	¼ Girth inches	Area Sq. Ft.
2	·028	8	·444	13½	1·266	19	2·507
2½	·043	8¼	·473	13¾	1·313	19¼	2·573
3	·063	8½	·502	14	1·361	19½	2·641
3¼	·073	8¾	·532	14¼	1·410	19¾	2·709
3½	·085	9	·563	14½	1·460	20	2·778
3¾	·098	9¼	·594	14¾	1·511	20¼	2·848
4	·111	9½	·607	15	1·563	20½	2·918
4¼	·125	9¾	·660	15¼	1·615	20¾	2·990
4½	·141	10	·694	15½	1·668	21	3·063
4¾	·157	10¼	·730	15¾	1·723	21¼	3·136
5	·174	10½	·766	16	1·778	21½	3·210
5¼	·191	10¾	·803	16¼	1·834	21¾	3·284
5½	·210	11	·840	16½	1·891	22	3·361
5¾	·230	11¼	·879	16¼	1·948	22¼	3·428
6	·250	11½	·918	17	2·007	22½	3·516
6¼	·271	11¾	·959	17¼	2·066	22¾	3·594
6½	·293	12	1·000	17½	2·127	23	3·674
6¾	·316	12¼	1·042	17¾	2·188	23¼	3·754
7	·340	12½	1·085	18	2·250	23½	3·835
7¼	·365	12¾	1·129	18¼	2·313	23¾	3·917
7½	·391	13	1·174	18½	2·377	24	4·000
7¾	·417	13¼	1·219	18¾	2·441		

To Use the Sectional Area Table

Suppose the length of a felled tree is 50 feet and its mid length quarter girth, over bark, is 6½ inches, then the volume over bark of that tree is arrived at as follows:–

6½ inch ¼ Girth = Sectional Area of ·293
Volume = ·293 × 50
= 14·650 Cubic Feet Hoppus Measure Over Bark.

These tables can be used if Hoppus Tables are not available.

APPENDIX 6

Equivalent Diameters for Quarter Girth

¼ Girth	Inches Diameter	¼ Girth	Inches Diameter	¼ Girth	Inches Diameter	¼ Girth	Inches Diameter
2	2·54	8	10·19	14	17·82	20	25·46
2½	3·18	8½	10·82	14½	18·46	20½	26·10
3	4·02	9	11·46	15	19·10	21	26·74
3½	4·65	9½	12·09	15½	19·73	21½	27·37
4	5·09	10	12·73	16	20·37	22	28·01
4½	5·73	10½	13·37	16½	21·01	22½	28·65
5	6·37	11	14·00	17	21·64	23	29·48
5½	7·00	11½	14·64	17½	22·28	23½	30·12
6	7·64	12	15·28	18	22·92	24	30·56
6½	8·27	12½	15·92	18½	23·55		
7	8·91	13	16·75	19	24·19		
7½	9·55	13½	17·39	19½	24·83		

Some Vegetation Types and Choice of Species for Planting

Old Woodland, Coppice, Foxglove and Willow Herb	Oak, Beech, Douglas Fir, Japanese Larch.
Bracken with grasses	Norway Spruce, Douglas Fir, and Scots Pine on drier sites.
Heather and Ling	Scots Pine at low elevations, Sitka Spruce and Lodgepole Pine mixture at high elevations.
Ling and Bracken	Exposed sites, Sitka Spruce and Lodgepole Pine mixture. Not exposed Douglas Fir.
Mat Grass	Japanese Larch or Sitka Spruce on turves.
Blaeberry and Ling	Japanese Larch or Sitka Spruce on turves, or Sitka Spruce Lodgepole Pine mixture.
Heath and Deer Grass	Plough or drain and manure using mixture of Sitka Spruce and Lodgepole Pine.
Molinia Grass	Sitka Spruce unless frosty, then Norway Spruce.
Rushes and Grasses	Norway Spruce or Sitka Spruce in North, possibly Oak in South.
Ferns, Grass, Foxglove, Bramble.	Oak.

INDEX

Age of Plants, 35
Alder, 2, 6, 22, 27, 85
Animals, 129
Area determination, 167
Ash, 2, 6, 12, 22, 27, 83, 111
Aspen, 23, 85

Beating up, 97
Beech, 2, 6, 12, 22, 27, 82, 110
Birch, 2, 22, 27, 83, 112
Brashing, 100
Brown Earth, 59

Cell types, 5
Chestnut, Sweet or Spanish, 2, 6, 12, 22, 27, 84
    Horse, 23, 27, 86
Cleaning, 101
Climatic factors, 63
Compartment, 39
Conversion, 146
Coppice, 38, 49
Cypress, Lawson's, 6, 20, 27, 78
    Monterey, 6, 20, 27, 79
    Nootka, 6, 20, 79

Diffuse porous, 4
Drainage, 50, 53
Douglas Fir, 2, 6, 12, 20, 27, 73, 109

Elm, 2, 6, 12, 23, 27, 86
Establishment, 99
Extraction methods, 143

Felling, 142
Fencing, erection, 46
    layout, 43
    materials, 42
Fibres, 4

Fire protection, 130
Form factor, 121
Fungi, 138

Grafting, 37
Gley, 61

Height measurement, 116
Hemlock Fir, 6, 12, 20, 27, 77
Hyponasty, 2
Hypsometers, 117

Increment, 128
Insects, 134

Larch, European, 2, 6, 12, 17, 27, 71, 109
    Japanese, 2, 6, 12, 17, 27, 72, 109
    Hybrid, 2, 6, 12, 17, 27, 72, 109
Layering, 37
Light demanders, 6
Lime, 2, 6, 12, 23, 27, 86, 112
Line ranging, 106
Lining out, 35

Maple, 2, 6, 12, 22, 27, 86
Manuring, 36, 97
Maturity, 12
Mixed woods, 66

Nursery fertility, 36
    heathland, 36
    site, 24

Oak, pedunculate, 2, 6, 12, 22, 27, 80, 110
    sessile, 2, 6, 12, 22, 27, 81, 110
    red, 81
Obstacles to chainage, 164

Parenchyma, 3
Peat, 54, 61
Photosynthesis, 6
Pine, Austrian, 2, 27, 71
   Corsican, 2, 6, 12, 17, 27, 69, 108
   lodgepole, 2, 6, 12, 17, 27, 70, 108
   mountain, 2, 27, 71
   Scots, 2, 6, 12, 17, 27, 69, 108
Pits, 3
Planting, density, 94
   methods, 88
   regularity, 95
   season 87
   tools, 88
Ploughing, 56
Poplars, 2, 6, 12, 23, 84, 111
Podzol, 59
Preparation of ground, 48
   of soil, 50
Preservation, 148
Pure woods, 66

Red Cedar, 6, 12, 20, 27, 78
Rendzina, 61
Reproduction, 12
Respiration, 7
Resin canal, 3
Ring porous, 4
Roads, layout, 39
Root suckers, 38
Rooting, types, 2

Sales agreement, 140
Sand dune fixation, 50
Seasoning, 148
Seed, collection, 17
   extraction, 16
   germination, 29, 30
   sowing, 26, 28
   testing, 26

Seedbed preparation, 25
   protection, 30
Seedlings, stocktaking, 31
Selection of species, 58
Shade bearers, 6
Silver Fir, Grand, 2, 6, 12, 20, 27, 76
   Noble, 2, 6, 12, 20, 27, 77
Soil, acidity, 28
   types, 58
Sowing densities, 27
Spruce, Norway, 2, 6, 12, 20, 27, 74, 109
   Sitka, 2, 6, 12, 20, 27, 75, 110
   Omorica or Servian, 20, 27, 75, 110
Surveying, line, 161
Sycamore, 2, 6, 12, 22, 27, 82, 111

Thinning, 104
Tracheids, 3
Transpiration, 8
Transplanting, 32
Types of trees, 101

Undercutting, 32
Utilisation, 152

Valuation, 128
Vessels, 4
Volume, of woods, 122
   production, 12
   quarter girth, 113
   true, 114

Weeding, plantations, 98
   seedbeds, 29